THE RISE AND FALL OF THE
DINOSAUR

THE RISE AND FALL OF THE
DINOSAUR

JOSEPH WALLACE

GALLERY BOOKS
An Imprint of W. H. Smith Publishers Inc.
112 Madison Avenue
New York City 10016

A Friedman Group Book

Published by
GALLERY BOOKS
An imprint of W. H. Smith Publishers, Inc.
112 Madison Avenue
New York, New York 10016

ISBN 0-8317-2368-8

THE RISE AND FALL OF THE DINOSAUR
was prepared and produced by
Michael Friedman Publishing Group, Inc.
15 West 26th Street
New York, New York 10010

Editor: Sharon L. Squibb
Copy Editor: Emily Loose
Art Director: Mary Moriarty
Designer: Robert W. Kosturko
Photo Editor: Philip Hawthorne
Production Manager: Karen L. Greenberg

Typeset by BPE Graphics, Inc.
Color separations by South Seas Graphic Arts Company Ltd.
Printed and bound in Hong Kong by Leefung Asco Printers Ltd.

DEDICATION

To my parents, for never asking, "So
when are you going to get a real job?"
Thanks.

CONTENTS

CONTENTS

WHY DO WE LOVE THE DINOSAURS?

Dinosaur footprints embedded in rock graphically indicate the creature's impressive size.

Black & white original courtesy American Museum of Natural History. Hand colored by R. W. Kosturko

Ever since the discovery of the first dinosaur fossil, these great reptiles have occupied a prominent place in both the public and scientific imagination. Reports on new dinosaur discoveries are consistently among the most popular subjects in magazines and newspapers, books about dinosaurs sell millions of copies, and science and natural history museums report that their dinosaur halls far outdraw any others. Scientists such as Nicholas Hotton, an eminent paleontologist at the Smithsonian Institute in Washington, D.C., have spent lifetimes pursuing the history of these mysterious and fascinating creatures.

Yet, when asked why the dinosaurs have inspired such ongoing fascination, even Hotton has a hard time explaining. "People can't get enough of dinosaurs," he agrees, and then adds, "but I haven't the slightest idea why." In fact, Hotton isn't even sure why *he* was fascinated enough to pursue a career studying extinct reptiles. "I grew up in upper Michigan, where there were no fossils," he recalls. "There weren't even any lizards. But, for some reason, I had no doubt that I was going to spend my life surrounded by dinosaurs and other ancient animals."

Hotton does, however, speculate that interest in dinosaurs is in part due to the fact that the great creatures lived so many millions of years ago, and in a world very different from the world as we know it today. "People love the past, the

Dinosaurs came in a variety of odd and fascinating shapes, from powerful two-legged hunters like *Tyrannosaurus* to this well-protected *Agathaumus* (below). Armed with three sharp horns and a spiny neck shield, *Agathaumus* roamed the plains of Wyoming 65 million years ago.

In toy stores, book sellers, and novelty shops all over the world, dinosaur paraphernalia is among the most popular items on the shelves. Ferocious looking even as a diminutive model, this inflated Tyrannosaurus towers over other dinosaur toys (right).

idea of a world without cities, without humans," he says. "So the mysteries of the ancient world hold an immense attraction."

As for interest in the dinosaurs themselves, they are probably so appealing because they were both so large and so unlikely looking. "They seem almost mythical," Hotton points out. "They don't seem quite real, so they appeal to everyone's sense of fantasy."

Whatever the reasons for their fascination, most people don't really know much about the crea-tures except what they can learn from the towering skeletons exhibited in museum halls around the world. Ask people what dinosaurs looked like, and chances are they will describe either a vast, blocky creature with a comically long neck and tiny head (the *Brontosaurus*) or a towering monster with dripping jaws and nightmarishly sharp teeth (the *Tyrannosaurus*).

They wouldn't be wrong: During the 160 million years that dinosaurs inhabited the earth, many species closely resembled those two great dinosaurs. Others, however, took remarkably different and even harder-to-believe forms. Some dinosaurs were covered with spikes and sported tails that ended in brutal clubs. Others had strong legs and could run at speeds of thirty miles per hour or more; they grabbed their prey with agile hands tipped with sharp talons.

Little as they know about the appearances of dinosaurs, most people know even less about dinosaur lifestyle, though the most surprising scientific research of recent

American Museum of Natural History

The sharp claws and fearsome jaw are strikingly apparent in the fossilized skeleton of the *Tyrannosaurus* pictured here (left). The dinosaur's awesome qualities have fascinated the public for generations and have made dinosaurs popular exhibits in many museums.

Although in reality *Stegosaurus* (left) and *Tyrannosaurus* (right) lived millions of years apart, in the Walt Disney film *Fantasia* (right) they romped together and enthralled the public to the dramatic music of Igor Stravinsky's "Rite of Spring."

years has focused on how the dinosaurs lived. Some, we now know, were caring parents, raising their young in nests and feeding and protecting them as they grew. Others apparently used tusks or horns to fight each other during mating rituals similar to the clashes that occur today between moose or caribou. And some ran in great herds, roaming across the ancient plains like the huge herds of buffalo that once inhabited the American West.

Dinosaurs have also remained in the public eye because along with every new insight into their lives come more questions, usually followed by a lively scientific debate. For example, why did the dinosaurs rise to such prominence, dominating all other creatures on earth? Some dinosaurs were fierce hunters; if they were cold-blooded, like today's slow-moving reptiles, how did they manage to hunt and kill with the sustained energy of a warm-blooded creature?

But no question is as mysterious or has provoked as much controversy as the riddle of the dinosaurs' extinction. Why, after 160 million years of preeminence among all living creatures did the dinosaurs completely disappear? Was their extinction, as some scientists argue, a natural and gradual process due simply to evolution, or was it the result of some cataclysmic occurrence, devastatingly and shockingly swift? If a catastrophe occurred, what was it? A deadly plague, a rain of comets hurtling to earth from beyond our Solar system? And could it happen again? Whatever truly motivates the public's fascination with the dinosaurs, the ongoing search for clues to these and other questions remains a wonderfully unpredictable and entertaining spectator sport for anyone interested in these long-gone giant reptiles.

THE ARRIVAL

The most basic biology lesson includes theories about the beginning of all life, when the murky primordial oceans gave birth to the first one-celled organisms. The history of how these tiny creatures became the great dinosaurs, and what lived in between, is a fascinating story.

Scientists today believe that the earth itself is about 4.5 billion years old, and that the first simple organisms, similar to today's one-celled bacteria, arrived about 3.5 billion years ago. Only over a vast period of time (many more years than from the arrival of the dinosaurs until the present) did these primitive organisms evolve into more complex animals, including primitive jellyfish and worms.

Obviously none of these early organisms bore any remote resemblance to dinosaurs, and it is hard to imagine how such tiny animals developed into such towering beasts. However, during the Paleozoic ("Ancient Life") Era, about 600 million years ago, the pace of evolution apparently quickened. Crabs, shellfish, coral, and other invertebrate animals (those with no backbones) populated the oceans in increasing number and variety until, about 500 million years ago, the first backboned sea creatures, fish, evolved.

The appearance of fish is relevant to the evolution of dinosaurs because it is from fish, scientists say, that the more sophisticated forms of terrestrial life evolved.

American Museum of Natural History

A large predatory creature armed with sharp teeth, the Dimetrodon was equipped with a sail-like fan that may have helped regulate its body temperature.

This invasion of the land began about 350 million years ago, when certain fish developed simple lungs, evolving into the first amphibians. Although they could leave the water, these amphibians, ancestors to present-day frogs and salamanders, were still far from well adapted for land life. Their skin was moist and sensitive to the sun; needing to return to the water frequently, they inhabited only shorelines or riverbeds. They also had to return to the water to lay their eggs, which would have quickly dried out without the water's protection. Although the amphibians were the first higher life forms to populate the land, they were several steps on the evolutionary ladder away from truly penetrating the rich land expanses.

The cold-blooded, thick-skinned reptiles that eventually evolved from these amphibians, an estimated 300 million years ago, represent the next great leap toward sophisticated life on land, and toward the evolution of dinosaurs. Their eggs, fertilized within the female's body, were covered in a tough coating that protected them from drying out once they were laid. Able to live and breed entirely on land, reptiles were the first vertebrates to spread across the vast, largely unpopulated continents.

Still, much time for evolution was needed before such great beasts as the Tyrannosaurus would emerge from these earliest foreshadowings. Most of this development took place as the Paleozoic Era gave way to the Mesozoic ("Middle Life")—about 225 to 250 million years ago. Fossils from this period offer extensive evidence to explain the evolutionary process that took place.

Over the ages, the first reptiles developed into several different groups, which scientists now classify according to the number and position of holes behind the eyes on each side of the skull. (These holes, which still exist today, are thought to make room for jaw muscles, as well as to lighten the skull.) One group, which had no skull holes, count among their descendants today's turtles and tortoises. The second, with a single hole high in the skull, include the *ichthyosaurs* and *plesiosaurs*, the great predatory reptiles that eventually returned to the water and ruled the oceans for tens of millions of years. They have no living descendants.

The third group, called the *Synapsids*, had a single opening low in the skull. They were a fascinating group of reptiles with many characteristics of today's mammals, and they were the dominant animals on land for more than 70 million years—until the rise of the dinosaurs, when they all died out.

The true mammals evolved from these mammal-like reptiles; unlike their ancestors, they survived alongside the dinosaurs. This survival was tenuous at best, however, with small shrewlike animals making up much of the mammal population throughout the reign of dinosaurs. The true age of mammals did not arrive until the great reptiles became extinct.

The fourth group, the *Diapsids*, which had two skull holes, gave rise to two main family lines. One eventually evolved into today's

One way scientists classify different types of reptiles is by the number of holes in their skulls. Turtles and tortoises had no holes; the swimming *plesiosaurs* had one hole high in the skull; the mammal-like reptiles also had one hole, but low in the skull. Two types of reptiles had two skull holes. One type evolved into today's snakes and lizards; the other type was the greatest of all reptiles: the dinosaurs.

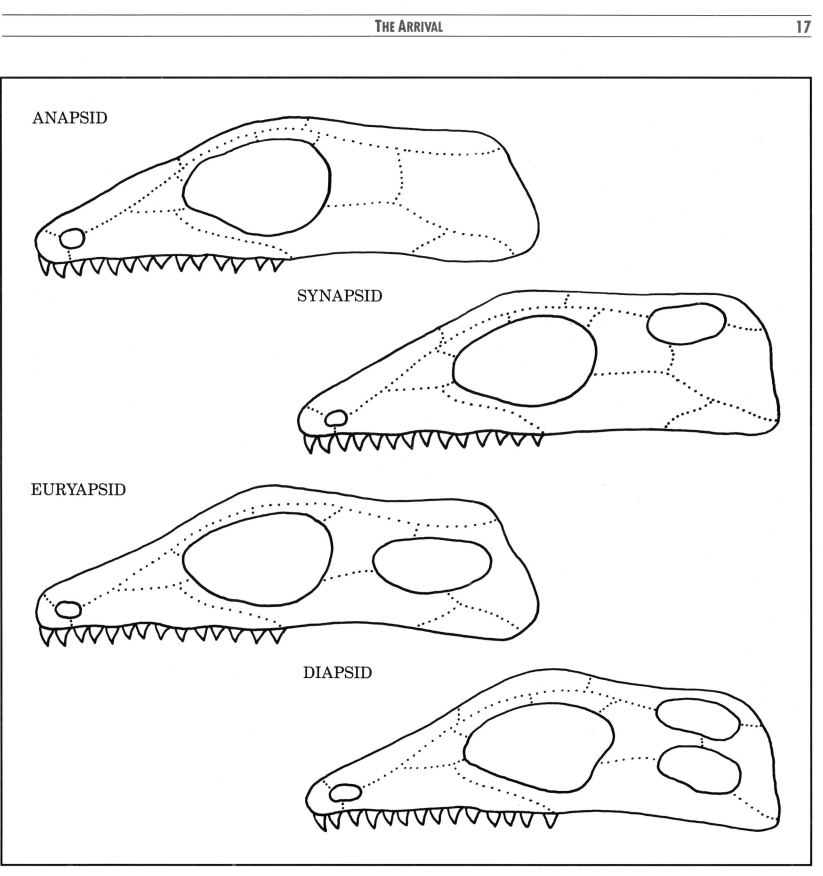

ANAPSID

SYNAPSID

EURYAPSID

DIAPSID

R. W. Kosturko

TIME LINE/FAMILY TREE

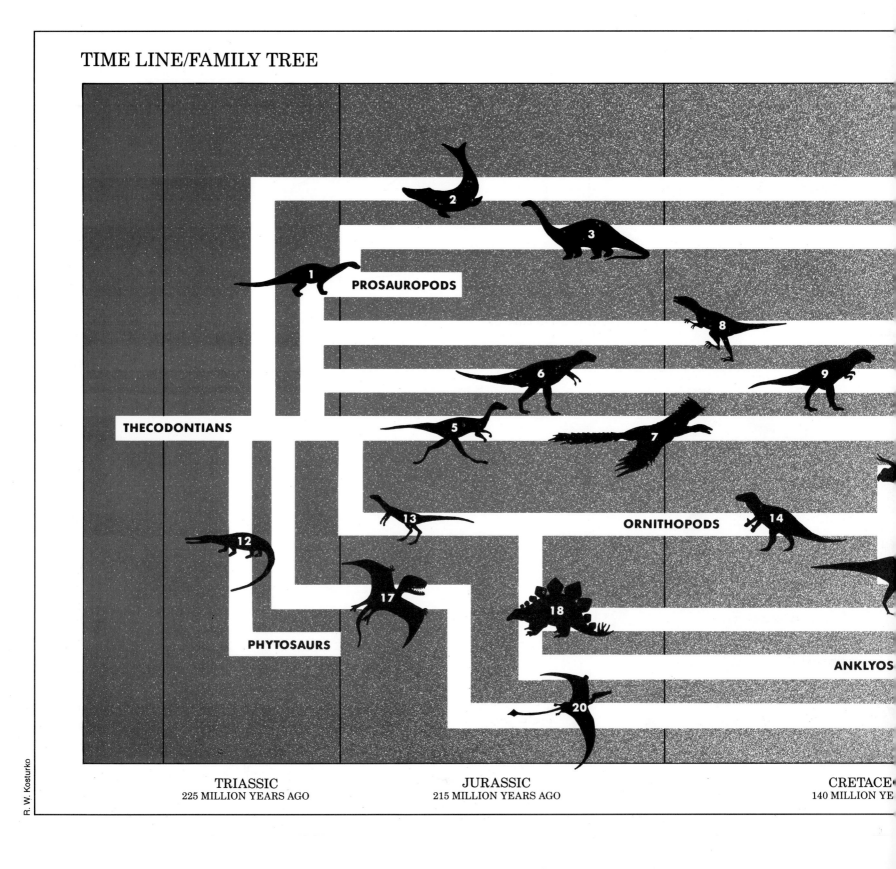

PROSAUROPODS

THECODONTIANS

ORNITHOPODS

PHYTOSAURS

ANKLYOS

TRIASSIC
225 MILLION YEARS AGO

JURASSIC
215 MILLION YEARS AGO

CRETACE
140 MILLION YE

R. W. Kosturko

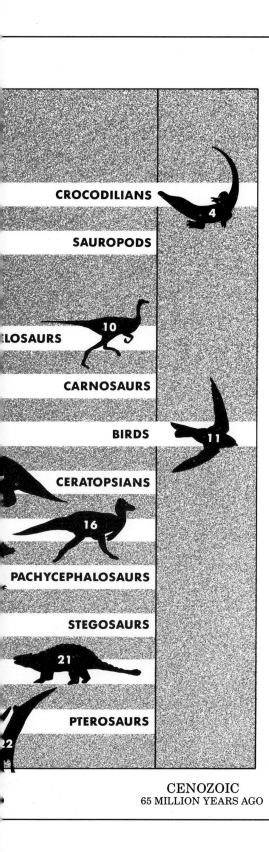

CROCODILIANS

SAUROPODS

...LOSAURS

CARNOSAURS

BIRDS

CERATOPSIANS

PACHYCEPHALOSAURS

STEGOSAURS

PTEROSAURS

CENOZOIC
65 MILLION YEARS AGO

1   Plateosaurus
2   Metriorhynchus
3   Diplodocus
4   Crocodile
5   Coelophysis
6   Megalosaurus
7   Archaeopteryx
8   Deinonychus
9   Tyrannosaurus
10   Ornithomimus
11   Bird
12   Rutiodon
13   Lesothosaurus
14   Iguanodon
15   Triceratops
16   Corythosaurus
17   Dimorphodon
18   Stegosaurus
19   Pachycephalosaurus
20   Rhamphorhynchus
21   Euoplocephalus
22   Pteranodon

The rise and fall of the dinosaurs has been well charted by scientists. At the end of the Triassic Period, the first *prosauropods* and others were beginning to appear. The Jurassic Period saw the emergence of numerous dinosaur species, many of which became amazingly abundant during the Cretaceous Period. Then, 65 million years ago, almost every dinosaur species on earth died out—and we still aren't sure why.

snakes and lizards. The other, although it dominated the earth for a remarkable 160 million years, did not evolve into any creatures that still survive today in any recognizable form.

The members of the latter half of the *Diapsid* family were dubbed the *archosaurs*, or "ruling reptiles." You'd need to look at the holes in their skulls to tell that the various archosaurs were closely related, because over the course of the eons some of them developed into slow-moving plant-eaters 70 or more feet (22 meters) long; others into towering predators with fearsomely sharp teeth; and still others into shambling creatures equipped with such effective defenses as long spines, armor plates, and tails equipped with spikes or clubs. We know them as the dinosaurs.

Both the birth and extinction of the dinosaurs—and many other creatures—took place during the Mesozoic Era. To help plot the rise and fall of the great reptiles, scientists have divided the Mesozoic into three periods: the Triassic, which lasted from 245 to 215 million years ago; the Jurassic (215 to 140 million years ago); and the Cretaceous (140 to 65 million years ago). These are arbitrary divisions, but they help us grasp both the great passage of time and the extraordinary changes that were underway during the dinosaurs' era.

For much of the Triassic Period, the dominant archosaurs weren't dinosaurs, but their direct forerunners. These were odd reptiles known as thecodontians ("socket toothed"), and they gave rise to all dinosaurs, as well as to the ancestors of today's crocodiles; *Ptero-saurs*, the great winged lizards that ruled the skies throughout the age of the dinosaurs; and, remarkably, birds. Think of the thecodontians as the root of an enormous family tree branching off in many directions.

The thecodontians, entirely carnivorous, were largely responsible for the decline and eventual extinction of the mammal-like reptiles and other competitors for food and space. Why were these socket-toothed reptiles able to dominate so thoroughly? The answer, scientists say, lies mostly in the structure of the thecodontians' bones.

Nearly all of the other primitive reptiles were "sprawlers," creatures whose limbs were not adapted for fast movement. Whatever their size and strength, they were best suited for plodding along at a steady pace—an efficient system only if the competition from other creatures was minimal. As importantly, over the millions of years that they survived, few sprawlers had any true defenses other than their teeth.

The thecodontians and later archosaurs took advantage of these evolutionary drawbacks, and the mammal-reptiles and others paid the price. Most thecodontians, by drawing their limbs somewhat beneath them and striding from the hips, rather than from the knees, were able to walk semiupright, much the way a modern crocodile can when it is angry or frightened. This enabled them to move more quickly and efficiently than their primitive competitors.

Eventually the dinosaurs grew even more adapted to their environment. Many became fully upright, striding on immensely powerful hind legs, while others became adept at leaping and climbing. Along with this new ease of movement came other evolutionary advantages. While some slow-moving creatures—including many thecodontians, which had once been the most agile reptiles on earth—never stood a chance against their more agile competitors, other dinosaurs were well protected with bony armor. Many dinosaurs equipped for eating plants rather than meat also appeared.

By the time the Triassic Period came to an end, the dinosaurs were the undoubted rulers of the land. And they would remain so for more than 100 million years.

Evolving from the same *theco-dontian* ancestors as the dino-saurs, the *Phytosaurus* and other crocodile-like reptiles thrived in wet, swampy areas. Today's alligators and crocodiles are among the most ancient creatures on earth.

LORDS OF THE LATE TRIASSIC

If technology ever leads to the invention of a workable time machine, and brave scientists are willing to operate it, the Late Triassic (which began about 225 million years ago) would be one of the most fascinating and mysterious eras they could choose to visit. Voyaging researchers would hardly recognize the world they would venture into as the same world they left. For one thing, the individual continents had not yet been formed; the earth was covered by one large land mass and one large ocean. Inhabiting this landscape would be an odd mix of familiar plants and animals and others having no obvious present-day descendants. For example, in that distant age, ferns abounded, but no grasses or flowering plants.

Moving slowly forward in time, the travelers would be able to witness great changes affecting *Pangaea* ("All Earth"), as scientists have named the one supercontinent, which very nearly circled the earth around the equator. The forces of continental drift, which to this day still move the continents an inch or two a year, were at this time slowly tearing the supercontinent in two. The land masses this division was to form are now known as *Laurasia* (which included what are today the northern continents) and *Gondwanaland* (composed of Australia, Africa, and the other southern lands).

During the Late Triassic, however, this subdivision of continents was just beginning. The animals

"Mogollon Highlands" © 1986 Petrified Forest Museum Assoc.

Reminiscent of Colorado's Grand Canyon, the Mogollon Highlands loom ominously in this volcanic landscape of the Triassic period.

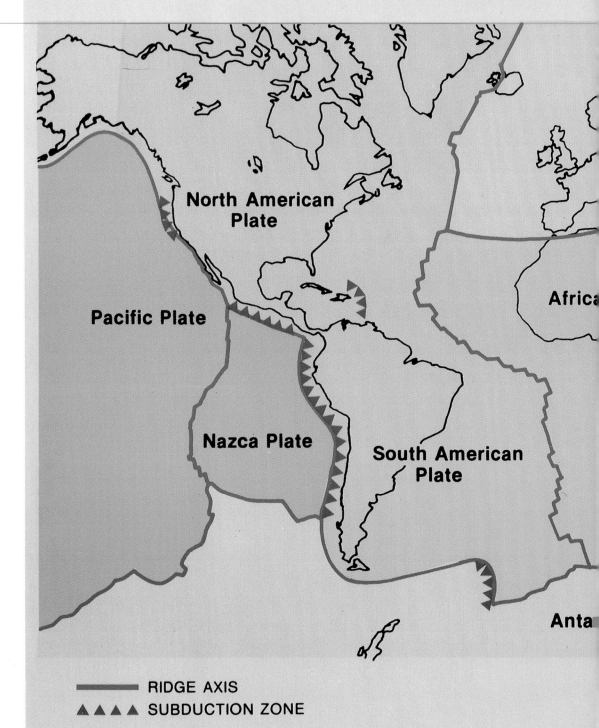

NASA

North American
Plate

Pacific Plate

Nazca Plate

South American
Plate

Africa

Anta

——————— RIDGE AXIS
▲ ▲ ▲ ▲ ▲ SUBDUCTION ZONE

Two hundred million years ago, all the earth's land was joined to form *Pangaea*, a single great supercontinent. During the age of the dinosaurs, however, the earth's tectonic plates shifted and pushed the continents into today's familiar shapes.

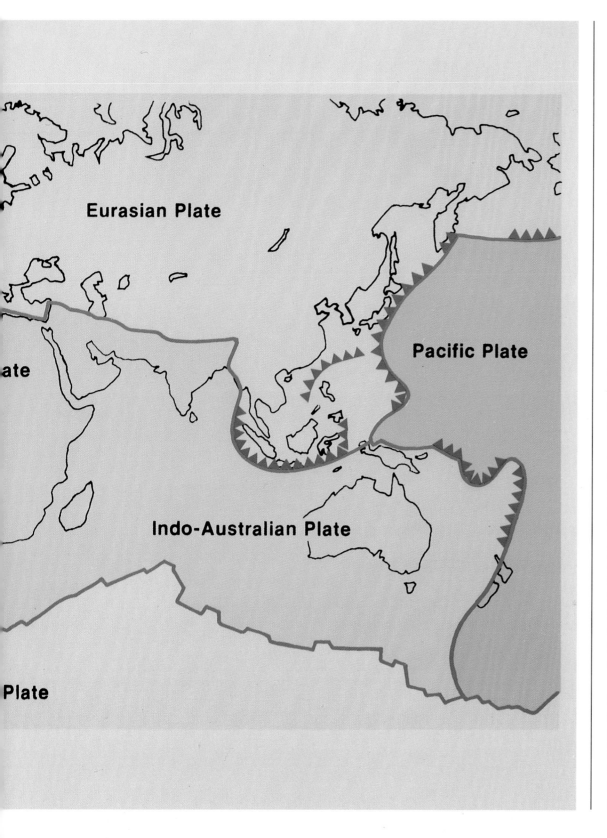

Eurasian Plate

Pacific Plate

Indo-Australian Plate

Plate

inhabiting the earth at this time, including the dinosaurs, could walk anywhere on this great land mass without crossing the one ocean, which covered most of the earth, and fossils show that many species inhabited all parts of Pangaea. In fact, remains of nearly identical dinosaurs have been found in such disparate places as North America and Africa.

Another difference travelers would notice is that because all of Pangaea lay near the equator, there was far less variation in temperature than there is now. Living in a warm, unvarying climate, dinosaurs did not need to hibernate, as mammals in temperate and colder climes do. In fact, they never developed any defenses against the cold—a fact that may well have contributed to their extinction 160 million years later.

Visitors to the Late Triassic would still encounter such ancient creatures as thecodontians and mammal-like reptiles, although these were already dying out. Primitive crocodiles and early frogs occupied the swamps, while lizard-like creatures could be found in drier areas. An observant explorer might even glimpse a few mammals, tiny inoffensive creatures that were hard-pressed to survive the onslaught of quick, agile, and well-equipped predators.

Much more noticeable would be the ichthyosaurs and *nothosaurs*, reptiles that had become so well-adapted to the oceans that their legs had become flippers, useless for anything but swimming. And soaring in the sky, with leathery skin drawn tight across their

Earth, during the Late Triassic, was mostly barren landscape with no grass or flowering plants and with comparatively few dinosaurs. Stalking through this scene is a tiny *Prosauropod*, one of a small group of dinosaurs that flourished at the time.

wings, were the first flying reptiles, called the *pterosaurs*.

The earliest dinosaurs, inhabitants of the Late Triassic, were not the familiar Brontosaurus or Tyrannosaurus that are the most popular exhibits in any natural history museum, but rather their smaller, less distinctive ancestors. Fossils of *Chindesaurus*, perhaps the earliest of all, were unearthed in Arizona's Petrified Forest National Park in 1986. Using a variety of techniques (including the precise measurement of the age of leaves and pollen found in the same rock), Robert Long of the University of California at Berkeley and his coworkers have judged that Chindesaurus dates back some 225 million years, to a time theorized as the very dawn of the Age of the Dinosaurs. It was, they think, a 200-pound plant-eater that walked on all fours.

Chindesaurus may well have been an ancestor of one of the most common Triassic dinosaurs, the *Plateosaurus*. This 25-foot (8-meter) vegetarian, a member of the widespread group known as the *prosauropods*, roamed over what is now central Europe; although it usually slogged along on four legs, it apparently could rise onto two, perhaps to reach tender shoots of leaves at the tops of trees. Other relatives of the Plateosaurus were far smaller, but probably none was more diminutive than the *Aristosaurus*, which measured only about 5 feet (1.5 meters) when fully grown. Its bones have been found in parts of southern Africa.

The Plateosaurus, and most other Late Triassic dinosaurs, belonged to the *Saurischia*, one of the two great dinosaur orders that evolved from the thecodontians.

The *Coelophysis*, may have been only three feet (one meter) long, but it was a powerful predator nonetheless. Its strong legs and slim shape allowed it to run quickly, and its needle-like teeth made short work of lizards and other small creatures.

Gregory S. Paul

The saurischians, or "lizard-hipped" dinosaurs, got their name from the structure of their pelvic bones, which closely resembles that of today's reptiles. They also often had sharp teeth, and many evolved oversized heads equipped for eating meat and carrion.

Among the saurischians were many of the most popularly recognized dinosaurs, including the Brontosaurus and all the great predatory dinosaurs (including the Tyrannosaurus and the *Allosaurus*). For the remainder of the Triassic Period, and for many millions of years longer, the saurischians were the most widespread and abundant of dinosaurs.

Perhaps the most successful lizard-hipped dinosaurs were the *coelurosaurs*—meat-eaters that ran on two legs. Among the coeluro-saurs were many of the most fascinating dinosaurs, including some in later periods that were possibly the most fierce dinosaur predators of them all, as well as a species considered to be the ancestor of the first true bird.

One of the earliest coelurosaurs was the *Coelophysis*, a small (3 feet [1 meter] tall), agile dinosaur with a wedge-shaped head and sharp, serrated teeth. Scientists think that this well-equipped predator chased after its prey, grabbing small lizards in hands that were set free by its upright posture. Remains of skeletons of baby Coelophysis, found inside fossil adults, indicate that the species' prey may have included its own young.

Not until the very end of the Triassic did the other great dinosaur order enter the picture. These were the *ornithischians*, or "bird-hipped" dinosaurs, many of which developed powerful grinding jaws and teeth well adapted to chewing plant matter. The ornithischians reached their peak both of variety and of numbers later, in the Cretaceous Period (which lasted from about 140 to 65 million years ago).

The first ornithischians to appear belong to the suborder *Ornithopoda*, which would later give rise to the abundant duck-billed dinosaurs of the Late Cretaceous Period. At the end of the Triassic, however, they were represented by dinosaurs like the *Fabrosaurus*, which were only about 3 feet (1 meter) long, and the slightly larger *Azendohsaurus*, both from Africa. Unlike the prosauropods that were the dominant dinosaurs of the time, these light-boned, long-tailed ornithopods had comparatively small arms and long hind legs adapted to walking upright.

Eventually, some of the bird-hipped dinosaurs would be among the most abundant dinosaurs on earth. There were relatively few dinosaurs of any kind at this time, however, in comparison to later, when great herds of dinosaurs rumbled across the continents. And the great plateosaurus, living during a time when there was little competition from other dinosaurs, would not survive to live on a more populated earth. They, as well as all other prosauropods, would soon become extinct.

The descendants of most other species, however, thrived throughout the coming Jurassic Period, the first that can properly be called the Age of the Dinosaurs. This 75-million-year period saw the first true flowering of the dinosaurs, an era in which the coelurosaurs and fabrosaurs were joined by hundreds of other dinosaur species, both bird and lizard hipped, including many of the strangest and most unfamiliar creatures of all.

A crocodile-like *Rutiodon* expresses its displeasure at a group of *Fabrosaurs* hurrying past. Small, lightly built creatures, the *Fabrosaurs* were among the first bird-hipped dinosaurs. Scientists think they ate the ferns and other plants that thrived during the Late Triassic.

One of the smaller stegosaurids, Kentrosaurus was covered with very distinctive spikes that were used to defend against larger predators.

THE SECOND AGE

After having witnessed the rise of the dinosaurs that occurred at the end of the Triassic Period, an intrepid team of time travelers would want to set their coordinates for the next great period of dinosaur history, the Jurassic (215 to 140 million years ago). The world they'd arrive in would be remarkably different from the one they left—due largely to the continued division of the earth's surface by continental drift.

By 150 million years ago, the supercontinents of Laurasia and Gondwanaland had been wrenched into now-familiar shapes: the first vestiges of the Atlantic Ocean had begun to form, separating the land masses that are now North and South America from the mass that eventually became Africa. Look at a map of the world today and you can still see how they once would fit together. And another major rift had begun in the breaking off of Australia from Antarctica. Yet, the continents had not yet divided enough to prevent the dinosaurs from migrating via land bridges from one continent to any other.

New types of animals were beginning to evolve at this time, adapting to fit the changing landscape. Dolphin like ichthyosaurs swam the oceans, and new species of pterosaurs continued to dominate the skies. Mammals could also be found, still mouse- and shrewlike. And plants—most importantly the *cycads* and *bennettitaleans,* which resembled palms—grew

Spanning more than 30 feet (9 meters) from head to tail, the huge *Yangchuanosaurus* was nearly as long as its name. This Jurassic predator lived in China and is believed to have been a fierce hunter who tore apart its prey with sharp claws and knifelike teeth.

nearly everywhere in the warm, swampy landscape of this time.

But alert visitors would focus most of their attention on the dinosaurs, the massive reptiles that came to rule the land as the Jurassic Period progressed. Among the dinosaurs that appeared during this time were early versions of the great predators, the plated dinosaurs, and many others equally fascinating. At the beginning of the Jurassic, saurischian (lizard-hipped) dinosaurs were still the most widespread, though ornithischian (bird-hipped) species became more and more abundant as the years passed.

While a few meat-eaters lived in the Late Triassic, the Jurassic saw the first large-scale appearance of the carnivorous dinosaurs. Some of the most fascinating were the small-to medium-sized coelurosaurs, descendants of the Triassic Coelophysis, who reached their full glory in the Jurassic. Coelurosaur means "hollow dinosaur," and indeed these species had lightweight bones, some of which were actually hollow—giving them speed and freedom of movement unknown to their plodding ancestors.

Coelurosaurs were, in fact, such active, fast-moving predators that many scientists now find it difficult to believe that they could have been cold blooded. Most cold-blooded creatures, including today's reptiles, tend to be slow moving; their blood is simply unable to supply enough oxygen to their muscles to sustain extended bursts of activity. Some scientists theorize, therefore, that the fierce bipedal coelurosaurs may have had

Ankylosaurs were among the strangest of all dinosaurs to appear during the Jurassic Period. They didn't move quickly, but their armored scales and club-like tails made them formidable opponents.

some sort of thermoregulatory mechanism similar to that of birds—or even mammals.

One of the best-known coelurosaur species is the *Coelurus*. No more than 7 feet (2 meters) long, it lived in the western United States and had a small head, long arms and comparatively slender hands. Scientists now believe it and the other coelurosaurs held their long tails off the ground as they ran, using them as counterweights for balance. A much smaller relative (but still apparently an efficient predator) of the Coelurus was the *Compsognathus*. Less than 3 feet (1 meter) long, this relatively tiny hunter apparently preyed upon lizards.

Some Jurassic predators were far larger and more impressive than the coelurosaurs, but none more so than the early *carnosaurs* ("flesh lizards"). This important group included some of the most powerful of all dinosaurs, massive creatures that towered over their prey. Perhaps the most famous Jurassic carnosaur is the *Megalosaurus*, one of the earliest of the large predators and also, in 1841, the first dinosaur to be officially named. Like the coelurosaurs, but far larger and heavier boned, this 30-foot-long (9 meters) dinosaur walked upright on its broad, four-toed hind legs. Each of its hands had three fingers tipped with strong claws, and its teeth were long, curved, and serrated. The Megalosaurus roamed over both supercontinents, but a particularly large number of their fossil remains and footprints have been found in southern Britain.

A close relative of the Megalosaurus was the Allosaurus, an even

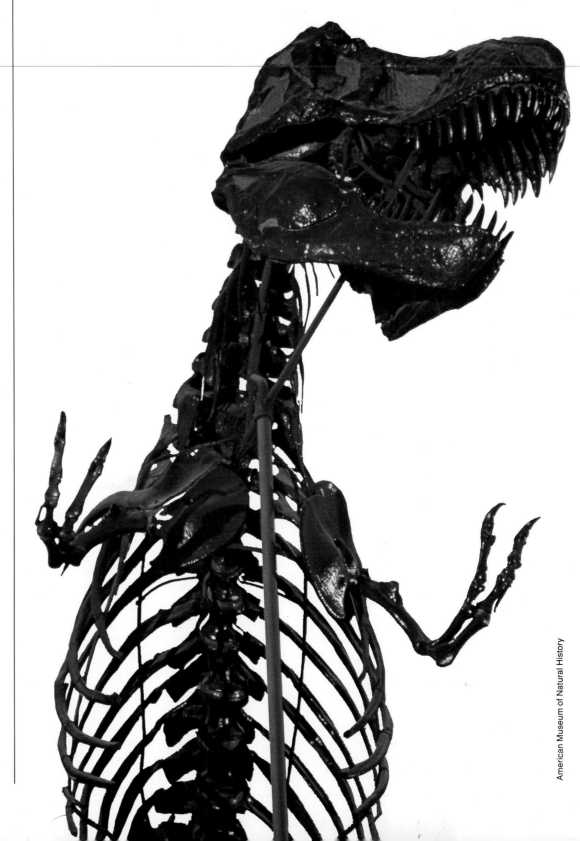

The *Carnosaurs* arrived in the Jurassic and lasted until the end of the Age of the Dinosaurs. They were among the largest and most fearsome of dinosaur predators. All the *Carnosaurs*, like this Cretaceous *Tyrannosaurus* (left), boasted rows of long, curved, sharp teeth and could overcome all but the most heavily armored dinosaur.

Until recently, it was widely believed that dinosaurs were plodding creatures. A century ago, however, painter, Charles R. Knight, provided a more accurate picture of dinosaur existence by portraying these *Dryptosaurs* (below) as quick, agile and active.

American Museum of Natural History

larger and more powerful meat-eater whose skeleton appears in the dinosaur halls of many museums. A remarkable 40 feet (13 meters) long and weighing as much as 2 tons (2.04 metric tons), this massive carnosaur was the dominant predator in Late Jurassic western North America, and its fossils have been found in a number of other locations as well.

The Allosaurus was so enormous that some scientists have begun to think it was just too bulky to be a good hunter. They suggest that, instead, it scavenged for food, finding and eating the bodies of Brontosauruses or other huge dinosaurs that had died of natural causes. Other paleontologists disagree, saying that the Allosaurus was extremely quick and agile for its size, and that it killed its prey with its knife-like teeth. Some dinosaur-hunters hypothesize that the Allosaurus may have hunted in packs—a terrifying thought even millions of years later.

Other Jurassic carnosaurs included some with odd features. The *Ceratosaurus*, for example, resembled its relatives, except for the presence of a small horn on its nose. No one is quite sure what purpose this harmless bump may have served; it may have featured in jousting matches between males attempting to impress a female.

The one characteristic shared by all carnosaurs was that they ate only meat. In contrast, another group of lizard-hipped dinosaurs that appeared in the Jurassic, the sauropods, shared an exclusively vegetarian diet. They were enormous, lumbering dinosaurs, de-

The 35-foot-(10.5-meters)-long *Allosaurus* was one of the Jurassic's largest and most powerful predators. And yet, the remarkable *Diplodocus* was even bigger. An amazing 90 feet (27.5 meters) in length, this *Diplodocus* may have depended on its great size and whiplike tail to protect it from *Allosaurs* and other meat-eaters.

scendants of the odd, partly carnivorous prosauropods of the Triassic Period, and included the familiar Brontosaurus. No one with any real interest in dinosaurs can forget that first view of a Brontosaurus skeleton in a museum, its endless neck, tanklike body, and tapering, impossibly long tail. Today, this dinosaur's silhouette is probably the most universally recognizable dinosaur image.

The Brontosaurus and its fellow sauropods shared more than diet. They were all built similarly, with four thick, pillarlike legs, a long, ponderous, heavy tail, and a swaying, snaky neck ending in a tiny head. They had comparatively weak jaws and flat, peglike teeth, and strangely, their nostrils were found high up on their heads. Although their brains were often no larger than a cat's, this lack of intelligence does not seem to have been a serious liability. In fact, they were so gigantic that most predatory dinosaurs seem to have left them alone.

Scientists once thought that sauropods spent most of their time in the water, buoying their massive bodies in placid lakes while grazing on the soft vegetation that grew in or near the water. Now, though, it seems that they lived mainly on dry land, using their long necks to reach succulent shoots at the tops of trees, even standing briefly on their hind legs to nibble particularly inaccessible leaves.

The sauropods lived throughout the Jurassic and Cretaceous Periods. Many of the most remarkable were found in the Late Jurassic, when they were extremely common

American Museum of Natural History

All *sauropods*, including the *Camarasaurus* (left), *Barosaurus* (center), and *Brontosaurus* (right), were once thought to spend most of their time in water. Now, however, scientists think they lived on land and used their long necks to reach leaves in the treetops.

This close-up of a *Brontosaurus* skull reveals the long, blunt teeth perfectly suited for eating plants. Its light, airy structure is a characteristic typical of *Sauropods*.

Perhaps the biggest dinosaur of all was the *Seismosaurus* (front) whose fossils were discovered in New Mexico in 1986. This *Sauropod* may have reached a length of 120 feet (36.5 meters) and a weight of more than 90 tons (82 metric tons), dwarfing even the 90-foot (27.5-meter) *Diplodocus* (back).

in Africa, North America, China, and elsewhere. No dinosaurs, before or after, grew to the monumental size or weight of the largest Late Jurassic sauropods.

While the 70-foot (21-meter) Brontosaurus ("Thunder Lizard") is by far the most famous sauropod, the *Brachiosaurus* was even larger and heavier. It weighed more than 80 tons (72 metric tons—that's 40 times as much as an elephant), and was remarkable among the dinosaurs for having front legs that were much longer than those in back. Visitors to the Natural Science Museum in East Berlin can get a look at one of the few nearly complete Brachiosaurus skeletons and view the structure of a creature that stands as tall as a modern four-story building.

For many years, most paleontolo-

gists thought that the largest sauropods reached about 90 feet (27.5 meters) in length and weighed about 80 tons (82 metric tons). Recently, however, researchers have dug up sauropod bones of creatures that may have truly dwarfed the Brontosaurus and its kin. A few years ago, the first remains of a sauropod that may have measured 100 feet (30.5 meters) in length and weighed 90 tons (92 metric tons) were unearthed. Startled scientists barely had enough time to give it the playful name *Supersaurus* before bones from an even larger sauropod turned up. This one, soon named *Ultrasaurus*, may have spanned 110 feet (33.5 meters). Then, in 1986, paleontologist David Gillette of the New Mexico Museum of Natural History in Albuquerque discovered the vertebrae of yet a larger sauropod in a rich New Mexican fossil site. Gillette named his find *Seismosaurus* and estimates that it may have been 120 feet (36.5 meters) long. So far, the Seismosaurus is the largest sauropod known.

While the lizard-hipped dinosaurs included some of the Jurassic's hugest plant-eaters and fiercest carnivores, many new bird-hipped species were also appearing at this time. Among the most interesting were the *ornithopods* ("bird feet"), the only ornithischians able to walk, or run, on their hind feet. Unlike the carnosaurs and most other bipedal dinosaurs, the ornithopods were plant-eaters. Most had horny beaks replacing the teeth at the front of their jaws, and their side and back teeth were perfectly adapted for grinding vegetation, their only food.

While the Cretaceous Period saw the height of the ornithopods' abundance, some of the most unusual species thrived in the Jurassic. Perhaps the most interesting was the *Heterodontosaurus*, which differed markedly from many of its relatives. This small, 4-foot (1.2-meter) dinosaur had three very different types of teeth: in the front of its upper jaw, it had sharp teeth, good for cutting plant material; behind these was a long canine tooth

Gregory S. Paul

that resembled a small tusk; and, finally, a set of flat, ridged teeth for grinding vegetation. Few other dinosaurs had more than one type of tooth, and only the Heterodontosaurus displayed such a tusk, the purpose of which scientists are still unsure. Perhaps, like the Ceratosaurus' horn, it was used in jousting matches between the males of the species.

Some of the speediest and most agile of all bipedal dinosaurs were another group of ornithopods, the *Hypsilophodontids*, and none of these was more impressive than the *Dryosaurus*. Living at the same time and in the same North American and African locations as the great carnivore Allosaurus, this fleet 10-foot (3-meter) plant-eater may have used its speed to flee from such ominous predators.

While these "bird-footed" dinosaurs and their relatives could show the quicksilver speed and agility of an antelope, other ornithischians were much slower moving. These were the armored, horned, and plated dinosaurs, who made up for a lack of speed by developing unmatched defenses of tough plates, sharp spikes and horns, and powerful clubs. Such protective devices must have caused a hungry predator to think twice before attacking.

Dryosaurus, a Late Jurassic bird-hipped plant-eater, may have used its powerful hind legs to flee from the *Allosaurus* and other predators of the western United States.

One of the largest (and, today, best loved) of these plated dinosaurs lived in Late Jurassic times. This was the *Stegosaurus*, the familiar, low-slung dinosaur with diamond-shaped bony plates running along its back and three-foot spines on the end of its tail. The Stegosaurus, first discovered in the late 1800s, reached a length of 30 feet (9.2 meters) and a weight of up to 2 tons (2.04 metric tons). It had a tiny head and a brain even smaller than most dinosaurs'. Presumably, it lumbered along, searching for the plants that made up its diet. If threatened, it might have used its tail as a defensive weapon, lashing out with its sharp spikes.

Although the Stegosaurus was discovered more than a century ago (ancient history in dinosaur-hunting terms), the odd plates on its back have kept it constantly in the news. The common image of this dinosaur—found in textbooks and museum exhibits—shows it with two rows of alternating plates running down each side of its spine. Now, however, scientists suggest that, in fact, only a single row existed. If proven true, this discovery may provide the key to the way the Stegosaurus managed to regulate its body temperature. The double row, experts explain, would be more useful for cooling the animal by channeling air along its back, another bit of evidence pointing toward the possibility of warm-blooded dinosaurs. A single row, by contrast, might allow the sun to strike the plates directly, helping keep a cold-blooded reptile warm for a longer period of time.

The Allosaurus, Brontosaurus, and Stegosaurus were just a few of the many dinosaur species that inhabited the world during the long Jurassic Period. But even greater diversity and abundance were still to come during the Cretaceous Period, which began about 140 million years ago. This was to be the dinosaurs' "golden age," the time of their greatest dominance, and ironically, also the era of their dramatic extinction.

Stephen Czerkas

One of the best known of all Jurassic dinosaurs was the huge *Stegosaurus* (left), who sported sharp spikes on its tail. The plates on its back—the position of which remains controversial more than a century after the *Stegosaurus* was first discovered—may have been used to regulate the great dinosaur's body temperature.

The *Stegosaurus* (above) was long believed to have slowly trudged across the Jurassic landscape, dragging its heavy tail behind. Recent research, however, shows that, like most of its contemporaries, this huge armored dinosaur may have been far more agile.

Ambushed by a herd of Alberto-saurus (left), these Anchicera-tops (center) use their horns to defend themselves while some Hypa-crosaurus escape (right).

THE FINAL FLOWERING

It is said that when the trunk of a fruit tree is girdled, the tree will quickly flower and produce one last crop of fruit before dying. Just such a burst of growth before death occurred in the history of the dinosaurs during the Cretaceous Period, spanning roughly from 140 million to 65 million years ago. Predatory carnosaurs, plodding armored dinosaurs, and plant-eating ornithopods found the Cretaceous environment welcoming and roamed across every continent in unparalleled abundance.

Yet, by the end of the period, this fertile environment changed in some way, and nearly all dinosaurs, new species and old, died out. A few scattered species may have survived the great and mysterious ex-tinction of 65 million years ago, but none were to last much longer. The great flowering of the dinosaurs in the Cretaceous was their last.

By the end of the Cretaceous, the forces of continental drift had pulled many of the continents into recognizable shapes, but there remained some major exceptions. For example, time travelers setting a course through the Cretaceous would find a shallow north-south sea splitting the supercontinent Laurasia into two parts: Asia-merica, containing East Asia and western North America, and Eura-merica, which would eventually become Europe and eastern North America. But three of today's continents—South America, Africa, and Australia—had already drifted

apart, although millions more years would pass before they reached their present locations.

Scientists believe that the Cretaceous (particularly the period's last years) was a time of great volcanic upheaval, when mountain ranges appeared and new islands were formed. The movement of the continents probably also brought on significant changes in weather conditions. In those land masses that were drifting closer to the earth's poles, the seasons became far more pronounced. The moist, eternally tropical warmth that had once blanketed Laurasia and Gondwanaland was now found only in isolated regions.

The formation of great mountain ranges as well as the arrival of harsher weather conditions in many areas meant that, for the first time, dinosaurs were not able to freely roam the entire length of the continents. For example, fascinating fossil discoveries reveal to us that many of the later families of dinosaurs, including some of the fiercest predators, odd horned and armored species, and ungainly "bird-footed" dinosaurs, developed only in Asiamerica.

Coinciding with the earth's shifting topography and drastic weather changes, familiar plants and animals first appeared. In early dinosaur history, plant life consisted mostly of ferns, palms, and cycads, but by the Late Cretaceous, flowering plants and trees had evolved. Such families as oaks and hickories spread rapidly, colonizing cooler areas where the more primitive plants could not survive. Reptiles such as tortoises, turtles, and

Flowering plants and trees made their first widespread appearance in the Cretaceous Period. *Pterosaurs* had been around for millions of years, but few were larger than those found throughout the Cretaceous like the one soaring here (left).

With the exception of dinosaurs, the animal and plant life of today resembled that of the Cretaceous Period. One would have easily recognized turtles, frogs, birds, or trees like these sequoias during the Cretaceous (below).

Doug Henderson © 1985

snakes were among the new species to first appear in the Cretaceous, while amphibians included early frogs and salamanders. Species of birds that evolved in the Cretaceous and are familiar today included primitive herons, gulls, and plovers. Though mammals such as opossums continued to thrive, they had not yet evolved into forms very different from those of earlier times. The mammals would not really develop or dominate until the dinosaurs had become extinct.

As millennia passed during the Cretaceous, the dinosaurs also evolved and multiplied. None were more widespread, abundant, and seemingly indestructible than the Cretaceous ornithopods, plant-eating relatives of the Heterodontosaurus and Dryosaurus of the Jurassic. Perhaps the most familiar of all ornithopods of the Early Cretaceous was the abundant *Iguanodon*, which can be seen in many museums around the world.

A bulky, 30-foot- (9.2-meter-) long dinosaur whose fossils have been found in North America, Europe, Africa, and elsewhere, the Iguanodon appears to have been adept at walking both on its hind legs and on all fours. Like many of its family, it had no teeth in the front of its jaw, only a hard beak designed for nipping off plants. The Iguanodon's main defenses against predators may have been its specially adapted thumbs, which were sharp and spiky. More likely, it depended mainly on acute vision, the ability to move quickly, and safety in numbers to protect itself against any large meat-eaters that attacked it.

Later in the Cretaceous, a

One of the most familiar of all Cretaceous dinosaurs is the *Iguanodon*, an early ancestor of the odd duck-billed dinosaurs of the Late Cretaceous. A 30-foot (9-meter) plant-eater, the *Iguanodon* had a sharp spike on each thumb, which were possibly used for fighting off predators.

strange new group of ornithopods appeared and soon became quite widespread. These were the *hadrosaurs*, or duck-billed dinosaurs, who survived in great abundance (especially in North America) until the very end of the dinosaurs' reign. In many ways, the duckbills held similar characteristics to such earlier ancestors as the Iguanodon. They too had no teeth in the front of their bony beaks and many grinding teeth in the back of their jaws. Their legs were longer and their tails flatter than the Iguanodon's, but the most dramatic difference was the presence of strange bony crests atop the heads of many—but not all—species.

These crests varied widely in shape and size from species to species. The *Lambeosaurus'* crest, for example, resembled a mitten, with the thumb pointing backward behind the creature's head. The *Tsintaosaurus*, in contrast, had a hollow spike like a unicorn's horn; its breathing passages ran up the inside of the spike. And the *Parasaurolopholus* had a tubelike, 5-foot (1.5-meter) crest that sprouted over its back. No one is completely positive what the purpose of these crests was. The best guess is that they featured in social behavior such as courting or fighting and that the hollow tubes may have allowed certain species to honk and bellow loudly and resonantly.

Observant scientists visiting the Late Cretaceous would notice striking similarities between the duckbills and such modern mammals as elk and caribou. Like these modern-day plant-eaters, the duckbills are thought to have traveled in

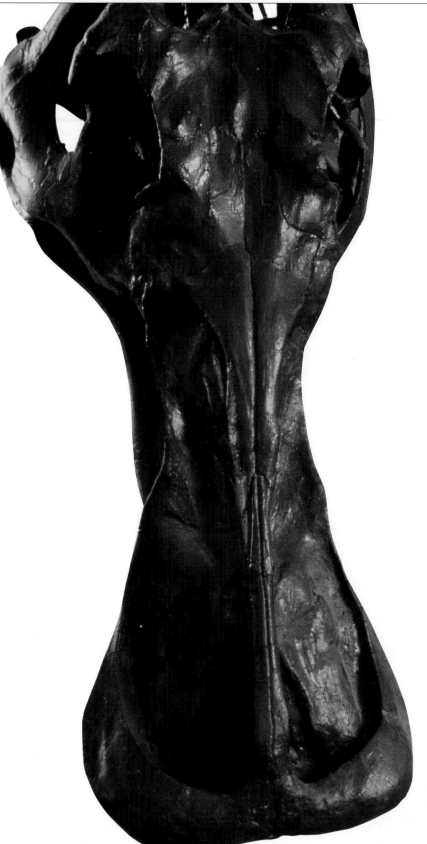

American Museum of Natural History

How strange were the duckbills? This is a skull of an *Edmontosaurus* (left), one of the least outlandish. Hundreds of teeth were crowded together in the huge jaw of this 40-foot (12-meter) dinosaur, enabling it to eat tough leaves and other vegetation.

Pachycephalosaurs, or ''bonehead'' dinosaurs, had skulls that may have been nearly a foot (30 centimeters) thick (right). Scientists believe that males banged their heads together in fights over females or in fights for dominance in a herd.

American Museum of Natural History

herds and presumably observed certain social patterns. Some may even have migrated to cooler regions in the summer to find food, then returned to milder areas as winter approached.

For a long time, scientists believed that duckbills lived much of the time in water, eating soft vegetation and using their flat tails to swim. The discovery of their arrangement of grinding teeth (with new ones constantly growing to replace others that were worn down) first suggested to researchers that the hadrosaurs must have eaten harder vegetation and therefore may not have lived in the water.

This theory was proved by one of the most remarkable dinosaur discoveries of all time.

In recent years, many fossils have been found of the *Anatosaurus,* a typical Late Cretaceous duckbill. In most cases (like most fossils), their remains consist of just bones, all soft tissues have rotted away before the skeleton fossilized. But scientists have recently found the remains of several fossilized Anatosaurus mummies, complete with skin and tendons. These remarkable finds were made possible by the extremely dry conditions of the dinosaurs' home territory (Alberta, Canada). When the duck-

bills died and gradually became fossilized, their skin and other soft parts, including their stomachs, dried out rather than decomposing.

Important discoveries awaited the researchers who studied the fossilized contents of the duckbills' stomachs. Contrary to expectations, they found that these reptiles' diet did not consist of soft waterweed, but of pine needles and cones and other tough foods. With this type of diet, the duckbills could not have been semi-aquatic creatures, although they probably did take to the water to escape predators, swimming strongly with side-to-side motions of their flat tails.

Hadrosaurus (left), shown in this 19th Century painting by Charles R. Knight, was the first duck-billed dinosaur discovered in the United States. Although scientists of Knight's era thought that duckbills lived in or near water, we now know that they actually ate vegetation found in drier areas.

Although recent research has shown that many duckbills lived far from water, they were strong swimmers and may have taken to lakes or rivers to escape from predators (right).

Doug Henderson © 1983   From "Maia, A Dinosaur Grows Up" John Horner, James Gorman Museum of the Rockies

While *Tyrannosaurus* is often pictured in illustrations as a stolid, heavy-bodied creature, it may actually have been a svelte, fleetfooted hunter—a frightening concept, given its 50-foot (15-meter) length, its powerful jaws, and its sharp teeth.

Duck-billed dinosaurs may well have been choice prey for the many meat-eating dinosaurs that roamed the earth during the Cretaceous. Among these Cretaceous predators, the great Tyrannosaurus, or "Tyrant Lizard," is probably the most well known. Up to 50 feet (15.3 meters) long and 20 feet (6.1 meters) high, the Tyrannosaurus would have towered over most earlier carnosaurs. This 7-ton (7.2-metric ton) meat-eater, the largest discovered to date, boasted a massive head equipped with serrated teeth that grew up to 7 inches (18 centi-

meters) long. Its front legs were tiny and weak and, unlike the Jurassic Allosaurus, it may not have used them at all, perhaps relying instead on its powerful hind legs to hold down its prey while it tore great hunks of flesh with its knife-like teeth.

Contradicting this terrifying image, some recent experts claim that the Tyrannosaurus, like the Allosaurus, wasn't the fearsome predator it's long been believed to be. In fact, they say, it was too large and ungainly to hunt successfully, depending instead on meals of car-

rion, the meat of dinosaurs that had already succumbed to illness or old age. This great meat-eater, so abundant in fossil deposits in Canada and the western United States, may have been the Late Cretaceous' vulture, not its tiger.

Other Cretaceous predators leave no doubt that they hunted living prey. The *Ornithomimus* was a medium-sized dinosaur with a long neck that reminded its discoverers of an ostrich. Its strong legs, perfectly adapted for speed, allowed this formidable meat-eater to chase after small animals as well as in-

sects, catching them with its agile hands. Oddly, the Ornithomimus had no teeth, but a horny beak instead. It probably crushed its food with its strong jaws just before swallowing it, much as many modern lizards do.

Even stranger was the huge *Spinosaurus*, a carnosaur that reached 40 feet (12.2 meters) in length. On its back the Spinosaurus boasted a sail-like structure made up of skin and bony spines, sprouting from the animal's backbone. This 6-foot- (2-meter-) tall tissue probably served the Spino-

The speed, agility, and power of *Tyrannosaurus* is vividly depicted here. Many scientists think the huge predator didn't use its tiny arms at all, but held its prey with a foot and tore it with its 7-inch (18-centimeter) teeth.

Gregory S. Paul

Thehe *Deinonychus*, or ''Terrible Claw,'' was far smaller than the *Tyrannosaurus*, but equally as fierce. Thirteen feet (4 meters) long, this predator used its superb sense of balance and remarkable ''switchblade claw'' to catch and disembowel its prey.

saurus as a regulating heat exchanger, stabilizing the animal's body temperature in both warm and cool weather.

Another Late Cretaceous hunter, whose saw-edged teeth were first discovered more than a century ago, shocked scientists when further fossil remains were found much more recently. The *Troodon* (''Wound Tooth''), according to these more recent discoveries, was apparently an ornithopod, related to such plant-eaters as the fleet-footed *Hypsilophodon*. But, unlike any other ornithopod—unlike any other bird-hipped dinosaur, in fact—the Troodon's teeth show that it was a carnivore. It is the only exception discovered thus far to the rule that all predators were indeed lizard hipped.

Without a doubt, the fiercest of the lizard-hipped predators were members of a small infraorder first discovered only twenty years ago. These were the *deinonychosaurs*, whose ferocity must have terrified any dinosaur confronting them. Scientists exploring the Cretaceous

would be well advised to keep a wary eye out for deinonychosaurs.

The best known of this group is the *Deinonychus* ("Terrible Claw"), a 13-foot (4-meter) dinosaur that ran quickly on its hind legs. This creature was armed with sharp teeth and wielded long arms ending in strong, clasping hands, each tipped with three sharp claws. Though many of its contemporaries shared several of these formidable features, the Deinonychus boasted a relatively large brain as well as a uniquely rigid tail, which gave it a superb sense of balance; both of these advantages contributed to its exceptional ability as a hunter.

But the Deinonychus had another weapon in its arsenal: an enormous, sickle-shaped claw on each hind foot. It would grab its prey with its hands, rear back on one leg (using its strong tail for balance) and slash at the prey's belly with the claw of its free leg. Few dinosaurs would have been able to withstand such an attack, because the Deinonychus may have hunted in packs, ambushing its prey.

Other Late Cretaceous predators shared the Deinonychus' methods of battle. The *Velociraptor* ("Swift Robber") was smaller (about 6 feet [2 meters] long), but no less equipped, with three-toed grasping hands and the same switchblade-like claws on its hind feet. Yet even dinosaurs of such fierceness as these were vulnerable. In 1971, researchers made a remarkable fossil find: the skeleton of a Velociraptor that had died while attacking a horned dinosaur called the *Protoceratops*. It seems that the predator had killed its prey by disembowelling it but that at the same time the Protoceratops, with its armored head, had somehow impaled Velociraptor, the two dying intertwined.

While the physiology and habits of the Deinonychus and most similar dinosaurs are well understood, those of one remarkable relative, the *Deinocheirus*, can barely be imagined. The single fossil find, a pair of arms excavated in Mongolia's Gobi Desert in 1965, has made this creature one of the most eagerly hunted dinosaurs of all. The arms of the Deinocheirus ("Terrible Hand") are more than 8 feet (2.5 meters) long, far longer than the arms of any other deinonychosaur. Each of the three fingers is tipped with a 10-inch (25.4-centimeter) claw, as long and sharp as a butcher's knife and curved to provide the maximum cutting edge. If the body of the Deinocheirus was in proportion to these arms, it must have been a truly terrifying predator.

With such fierce predators roaming every continent throughout the Cretaceous, plant-eating ornithischians would have been helpless had they not developed special defenses. While the duckbills may have escaped by adapting to the water, evolution provided other slower-moving dinosaurs with ingenious forms of protection against marauding carnivores—ironically making the Late Cretaceous the golden age of the horned and armored dinosaurs.

The *Chasmosaurus* had one of the longest neck frills of any horned dinosaur. As this painting shows (right), however, the frill was neither as thick or as heavy as it looked. Covered by skin and blood vessels, much of it was hollow.

Only a well-armed dinosaur like this *Triceratops* (below) would fight back against a *Tyrannosaurus*. Apparently the 30-foot (9-meter) plant-eater often clashed with the great predator. The Triceratops' sharp horns sometimes enabled it to emerge victorious.

Gregory S. Paul

Perhaps the most abundant family of these defense-adapted ornithischians in the Late Cretaceous were the *ceratopsians* or horned dinosaurs. The *Triceratops*, the largest and best known of this group, roamed in great herds across western North America, a sight that for drama must have surpassed even the great bison migrations of the nineteenth century. Thirty feet (9.2 meters) in length, weighing up to 6 tons (6.2 metric tons), Triceratops boasted a massive head, protected by a thick neck frill and armed with three long, sharp spikes. These characteristics alone would have protected the Triceratops from most potential predators. In addition to these defenses, and unlike its armored and plated relatives, however, the Triceratops was able to move quickly, making it difficult prey indeed for even the fiercest of predators. Other lesser-known ceratopsians had even more unusual arrays of neck frills and horns. The *Pentaceratops*, for example, had five horns, while the *Styracosaurus'* neck frill was made up of long, curving spines.

Outlandish as descriptions of the ceratopsians sound, these defense-laden dinosaurs were not the strangest creatures of their times. The *ankylosaurs*, or armored dinosaurs, featured far more elaborate defenses than even the oddest ceratopsians, usually including a combination of plates, spines, spikes, and ridges. This nearly impervious armor compensated for the ankylosaurs' lack of speed; squat and quite slow moving, they could nonetheless graze the plains in reasonable safety.

Gregory S. Paul

Albertosaurus (right) was a powerful predator, but it was probably no match for a herd of the horned *Monoclonius* with the long spines on their neck frills and their single sharp horns.

Because of its enormous neck frill, the *Chasmosaurus* (left) presented an odd sight. Travelling in herds, it may have found safety enough in numbers and speed to fend off *Tyrannosaurus* and other predators sharing its western North American habitat.

Gregory S. Paul

For example, the 30-foot *Ankylosaurus* itself was entirely covered in thick, bony armor, with spines protecting its head and a mass of bone forming a club on its tail. If menaced, it probably crouched to protect its soft underbelly and swung its club to ward off attackers.

The Tyrannosaurus, Triceratops, and Ankylosaurus were all the largest and best-equipped dinosaurs of their kind. All lived in the Late Cretaceous, a period of dino-saur dominance, in numbers that continue to startle paleontologists exploring new fossil beds. And all survived for millions of years. Yet even with such illustrious credentials and records of survival, all three died out suddenly at the very end of the Cretaceous Period, as did almost every dinosaur on earth. The search for the cause of this dramatic extinction has fueled an ongoing debate among paleontologists and other scientists through-out the world, and no doubt will for many years to come.

Though the story of the dinosaurs' death may remain a mystery, in the process of its pursuit, scientists continue to discover details of the dinosaurs' lives, bringing an almost mythical conception of the creatures closer to reality. For those of us who find the lives of the creatures hard to envision, scientists are beginning to bring us "home movies" of dinosaur life.

THE PRIVATE LIFE OF THE DINOSAUR

Doug Henderson © 1985 Collection of Los Angeles County Museum of Natural History

Scientists can learn a great deal by studying the fossilized bones of dinosaurs. A nearly complete Tyrannosaurus skeleton, before being mounted in a museum, will have provided researchers with a wealth of information. Not only can scientists estimate a dinosaur's size and strength from its fossils but with closer study, they can determine whether it walked on two or four legs, and whether it ate flesh, soft fruit, or coarse leaves. Although not as reliable a dating method as observing the rings in a tree trunk, the placement of its bones in layers of rock indicates when a dinosaur lived, as well as what other dinosaurs were its contemporaries.

As invaluable and as revealing as they are, fossil discoveries did not, until recently, provide scientists with solid answers to such extremely important questions as: What sort of family life did the dinosaurs have? Did some species have a social structure, like many modern animals? What color were they? As Hotton of the Smithsonian comments, "Sometimes it's hard to remember that the dinosaurs were living creatures, with social behavior that must have been fascinating." Hotton and paleontologists have long attempted to describe the world of the dinosaurs more thoroughly.

Early scientists, relying on the few fossils discovered, painted a dull picture of dinosaur life—stating that dinosaurs were gray or brown creatures that moved slowly

Stephen Czerkas

A 30-foot (9-meter) adult *Maia-saura* (right) keeps an eye on her nestlings, who have recently hatched within a mound formed by their mother. Paleontologist, John R. Horner, found evidence of this fascinating aspect of dinosaur social life in 1978.

This young duck-billed *Maia-saura* ("Good Mother Lizard") peeking through the underbrush (above) may have spent the early years of its life under the protection of its mother and other adults in a remarkable many-family nesting colony.

and lived nearly solitary lives. Scientists once claimed that certain well-known species, such as the Brontosaurus and other sauropods, were too heavy to walk on land and spent most of their sluggish lives lolling in the water. They also believed that all dinosaurs, like most modern reptiles, laid and then immediately abandoned their eggs, leaving the newly hatched young to fend for themselves.

Museum dioramas and early books on dinosaurs helped promote these "facts," which often weren't based on concrete research, but rather on a patchwork of guesses, hypotheses, and prejudiced judgments. Some of these conclusions were so widely believed that many paleontologists actually chose to ignore contradictory findings, immediately assuming that anything

challenging the accepted wisdom must be wrong.

Perhaps the most striking example of convenient disavowal involved the mummified Anatosaurus discussed in Chapter Five. In 1922, when scientists first discovered that this specimen's stomach contained pine cones and other dry-land vegetation, experts paid no attention to the implications of the evidence. After all, everyone "knew" that duck-billed dinosaurs spent most of their time in water. They resembled ducks, didn't they? Not until 1964, when paleontologist John Ostrom of Yale's Peabody Museum of Natural History reanalyzed the initial report, was the enlightening conclusion reached that the Anatosaurus—and probably all duckbills—were actually land dwellers.

Ostrom is just one of many scientists who are currently attempting to clarify our picture of the dinosaur's private life. Another is John R. Horner, paleontologist at Montana State University's Museum of the Rockies, who has produced fascinating and telling evidence suggesting that some dinosaurs lived complex family lives. In 1978, Horner and his research team stumbled upon evidence that the grasslands of northern Montana might be hiding one of the great finds of all time: a fossil bed of baby duck-billed dinosaurs, whose skeletons, like those of the young of so many species, had been nearly absent from the fossil record. What they found after they began digging, however, was an even more significant discovery than they had previously expected.

The researchers unearthed a scooped-out mud nest containing 15 fossilized baby dinosaurs. The babies, which were each about 3 feet (1 meter) long, showed evidence that they were not newborn, but had continued to occupy the nest as they grew. Horner and his team eventually found hundreds of whole or broken eggs and dozens of skeletons ranging from infants to full-growns. Near this first nest were many others, indicating that the site was an actual breeding colony of these dinosaurs, which Horner named *Maiasaura*, or "Good Mother Lizard."

Unearthing such abundant remains of a new dinosaur would be monumentally exciting in itself. Finding a colony of nests, containing dinosaurs of every age, was a break-through discovery, for it pro-

Doug Henderson © 1984

Not only parents and hatchlings (left) are found in the vast Montana *Maiasaura* colony, but skeletons ranging from new-born to adult. The dinosaurs may have nested together for protection against roaming predators, much as many birds do today.

Baby *Maiasauras* (right) naturally resembled their parents, as this hatchling skeleton shows. Their strong hind legs, fine-boned hands, and powerful grinding jaws equipped them for foraging among the plants of Late Cretaceous North America.

vided the first evidence that dinosaur parents actually cared for their young. For some time after birth, the babies would stay at the nest while the parents foraged, bringing back leaves and other plant matter for food until the young were large enough to roam safely on their own. The Maiasaurs, it seems, may have nested communally for the same reason that birds such as cormorants and penguins do today: Their numbers provided protection from predators.

While the remarkable insights into dinosaur behavior provided by the Maiasaurs are the fruit of a remarkably complete archaeological find, other recent discoveries have come only from meticulous laboratory work—through careful study of the great reptiles' fossil remains. Laboratory research has, for example, begun to answer many questions about the dinosaurs' sensory mechanisms, their intelligence, and the ways they moved.

Scientists have long known that dinosaurs had remarkably small brains for their great size, from which knowledge has evolved the popular conception of dinosaurs as terribly stupid, shambling, semicomatose hulks. Though no paleontologist will argue that the great reptiles were as intelligent as many of today's mammals, the dinosaurs' 160-million-year reign has led many researchers to look for ways in which the reptiles compensated for their apparent lack of brainpower. "Nothing survives as long or as successfully as the dinosaurs did without showing intelligence and adaptability," says Hotton.

Jurassic *Camarasaurs* (foreground) and *Camptosaurs* trudge through a large expanse of mud. The resulting fossilized footprints—called trackways—give scientists vital information on the living conditions and travelling speed of dinosaurs.

Research now indicates that one factor in the dinosaurs' exceptionally long survival was the development of extraordinarily well-adapted senses. Scientists now believe that the animals had acute vision, a keen sense of smell, and excellent hearing. For the predatory Deinonychus attempting to ambush a herd of duckbills, these well-developed senses would have been crucial, though no more so than for the fleeing plant-eaters they meant to devour.

Laboratory study of the skulls and odd crests and horns of the hadrosaurs, or duck-billed dinosaurs, indicates that many duckbills may have had powerful barking or grunting voices, and that when attacked, they used these voices to warn each other, much as zebras, wildebeests, and other modern prey species do when threatened.

No study, however, has given researchers more insight into dinosaur behavior than the examination of footprints—both individual prints and, more revealing, entire trackways. These tracks were made when dinosaurs walked on drying mud, their footprints eventually becoming fossilized. These fossils can reveal an incredible amount about dinosaurs' individual body motion as well as their social lives. For example, the spectacular trackways preserved in Connecticut's Dinosaur State Park vividly show the steady stride of dozens of *Eubontes*, mysterious Jurassic dinosaurs.

Perhaps most interestingly, dinosaur trackways have proven that some types of dinosaurs were communal, traveling in large herds. Multiple tracks headed in the same direction indicate that the Triceratops, Iguanodon, and others may have migrated long distances in search of food. Today, African antelopes and other mammals travel in a constant, circular migration over hundreds of miles of the Serengeti Plains of Tanzania and Kenya, bringing with them a contingent of predators and scavengers. It is not unlikely that certain dinosaurs migrated in similar fashion millions of years ago.

This conception of dinosaurs as herding animals also suggests further possible patterns of dinosaur life. For example, almost all modern herding mammals have devised fascinating rituals to determine which male will serve as patriarch of the herd. Bighorn sheep crash into each other with stunning force; sea lions wage bloody battles;

deer and moose use their antlers in sparring matches. It seems probable that dinosaurs engaged in similar rituals, which may explain the presence of small horns and other seemingly superfluous appendages.

More explicitly, footprint findings have indicated what types of terrain certain dinosaurs preferred. Trackways proved that the familiar conception of the Brontosaurus and other sauropods as semi aquatic creatures was incorrect; these great beasts had no problem plodding along on the land, actually preferring it to the swamps we have long pictured them in.

Scientists studying the distance between footprints have also been able to determine how fast many dinosaurs were able to move. Unsurprisingly, Brontosaurus and other sauropods weren't fleet of

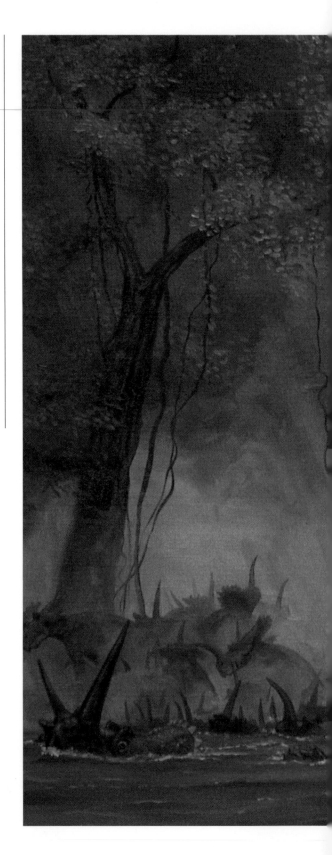

Trackways have enabled scientists to discover that many horned dinosaurs (including these *Centrosaurs*) traveled in great herds, much in the same way as caribou and wildebeeste do today. They may have migrated long distances in search of food.

foot, achieving top speeds of only five miles (8 kilometers) per hour. Other dinosaurs, however, moved far more quickly. Fastest were some of the small carnivores, which sped along as fast as 35 miles (56 kilometers) per hour. If they were around today, they could outrun a human, though not either a horse or dog. In general, the bigger predators were probably slower, and the herbivores slowest of all, but nearly every dinosaur seems to have been swifter than was once thought.

No matter how much fossil research has so far revealed to scientists, some questions about dinosaurs seem destined to remain mysteries. For example, although no one still insists that all dino-

Who knows what colors dinosaurs really were? Instead of the dull greys and browns of their traditional garb, many species may have sported bright reds, greens, and yellows similar to some of today's lizards.

saurs were the same shade of slate gray, their true color is still unknown. Because today's reptiles range in color from black to bright green to yellow, there's no reason to think that dinosaurs didn't exhibit similarly spectacular variations of color. The one clue to this question found, the fossilized skin of the Anatosaurus mummy, is covered with intriguing speckles that are perhaps the last remnants of some elaborate color pattern. No doubt only further astonishing fossil discoveries and further meticulous laboratory investigation of them will even begin to crack this and other secrets most likely ensconced in some form in the ancient and unyielding stone.

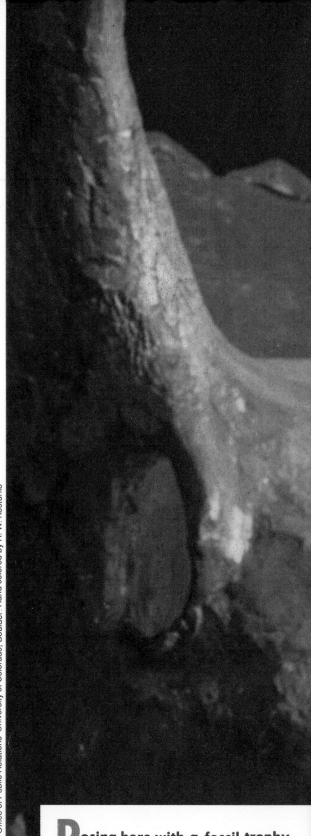

C H A P T E R 7

WARM BLOOD OR COLD TRADITION?

The theory was so simple and logical that for decades it was accepted nearly without question: Because dinosaurs were reptiles and all modern-day reptiles are cold-blooded, scientists concluded that all dinosaurs and other reptiles must have been cold-blooded too. Despite the fact that this theory was based on logical assumption rather than on evidence, even experts did not perceive the need to scientifically prove it. Just as the experts ignored solid evidence (in the form of the mummified Anatosaurus' stomach) that duckbills lived and ate on land, experts in this case ignored a lack of solid evidence, preferring to simply believe what they *thought* to be true.

In the 1960s, however, an era of new excitement and activity in paleontology, some scientists began to challenge this assumption, claiming that dinosaurs may well have been warm-blooded and calling for hard evidence. Perhaps the strongest and most persistent challenger has been paleontologist Robert T. Bakker of the University of Colorado Museum in Boulder. "I have never seen any believable evidence that dinosaurs were cold-blooded," says Bakker. "That theory rests entirely on tradition—so we simply cannot accept it on face value."

Indeed, even this long-standing "fact" was not always so widely accepted. As Bakker subsequently points out, "As far back as the 1830s, when scientists were first beginning to reconstruct dinosaurs

J. Martin Natvig/Office of Public Relations University of Colorado, Boulder. Hand colored by R. W. Kosturko

Posing here with a fossil trophy, Robert Bakker is one of the world's leading paleontologists.

The *Stegosaurus* remains a figure of controversy in the ongoing battle between scientists who believe that dinosaurs were warm-blooded and those who disagree. The placement of the plates along its back has been used as evidence by both sides, and so, the debate continues.

from fossils, many thought the dinosaurs were warm-blooded," explaining, "It was only later that this theory fell into disrepute."

Yet many other scientists, including the Smithsonian's Hotton, have even recently argued equally forcefully for the traditional view. When asked why this lively debate is considered to be one of the most important in all of paleontology, Bakker explains, "Because which answer you believe plays an enormous role in how you think the dinosaurs lived."

Were the dinosaurs in fact cold-blooded, the slow-moving Brontosaurus, lumbering Stegosaurus, and all others would have lacked, by definition, the ability to regulate their own body temperatures—depending instead on the warmth of their tropical surroundings as a

type of exterior heat control. Such an inefficient method of heat-regulation would have strictly limited the dinosaurs' peak periods of hunting or foraging. In order to escape temperature extremes at night and in cool weather, for example, they would have had to become comparatively inactive and at midday would have had to seek shade to keep from overheating.

Were the dinosaurs warm-blooded, however, they would have been capable of maintaining a pace of activity and of living in climates previously thought restricted to them. By burning up to 90 percent of their food to create energy, and using fur, feather, or fat insulation to prevent the resulting heat from escaping, present-day birds and mammals are able to stay active at times and in places that would kill

Cold-blooded animals, like this Triassic *Phytosaur* (above) and modern-day reptiles, require much less food for survival than warm-blooded predators such as lions or wolves. However, they have less endurance and are much more vulnerable to extremes in temperature.

If they had warm blood, these *Tyrannosaurs* (right) and other predators would be able to pursue *Maiasaura* more actively and ferociously. Many scientists believe, however, that the evidence fails to show that dinosaurs were warm-blooded.

cold-blooded creatures. Some researchers, in fact, contend that the early shrew like mammals, contemporaries to the dinosaurs, survived by being largely nocturnal, searching for food during the cool nights when the predatory dinosaurs, were they cold-blooded, would have had to be inactive. Today, birds and mammals have colonized the Arctic and other frigid areas where no reptiles are found.

In addition to being able to live in colder climates, warm-blooded animals can produce more energy over a longer period of time than cold-blooded species, foraging longer and moving faster than even a sun-warmed reptile. All this heat production, however, has its price: A predatory mammal must eat up to ten times as much food as a reptile of similiar size. Therefore, it must depend on a much higher population of food animals to survive.

Due to warm-blooded predators' need for a higher food population, Bakker reexamined the fossil record for possible evidence that dinosaurs were warm-blooded. His investigations centered around the premise that if very few dinosaur predators were found among huge groups of prey animals, these predators must have needed large quantities of food, and were therefore likely to have been warm-blooded. If the ratio was smaller, then the dinosaur predators were likely to have been cold blooded, like modern reptiles.

The investigations have revealed that the populations of many predatory dinosaurs *are* very low compared to the number of their apparent prey in most fossil beds, which

Gregory S. Paul

would appear to tilt the argument toward the theory of warm-bloodness. Unfortunately, as Hotton and other researchers have stressed, fossil finds can often be interpreted in many ways. For example, differences in habitat or bone structure may have made the bodies of plant-eaters more prone to fossilization than those of predators, providing an alternative explanation for the high ratio of prey to predator in many fossil beds. Further, any predator-prey ratio is suspect, because it is impossible to prove which species were the preferred prey of an area's predators.

Other fossil findings may, however, prove more conclusive. John Ostrom of Yale's Peabody Museum of Natural History, Bakker, and others have produced new evidence indicating that at least some dinosaurs may have had the means to regulate the temperature of the blood pumping through their veins. One of the most persuasive arguments has to do with the ruling reptiles' posture, the very physiological detail that scientists have used to separate the dinosaurs from other early reptiles. All dinosaur forerunners—as well as all modern reptiles—spent most of their time sprawling, with their legs to the sides of their bodies, close to the ground. Their posture did not allow them to stand upright. But as described in Chapter Two, some dinosaurs (including Tyrannosaurus and all duckbills) *were* able to achieve a fully erect posture, with their legs positioned directly beneath their torsos.

The only animals in our time equipped to enjoy this important

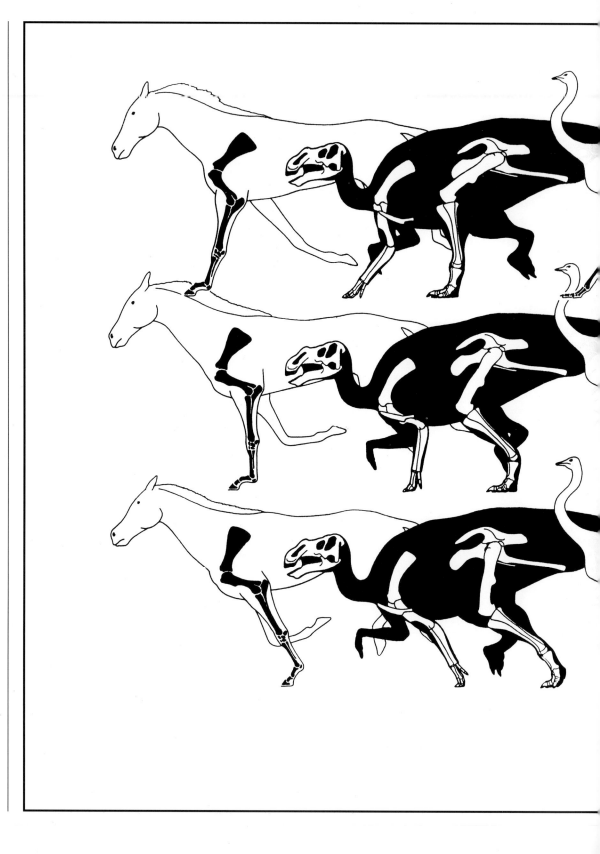

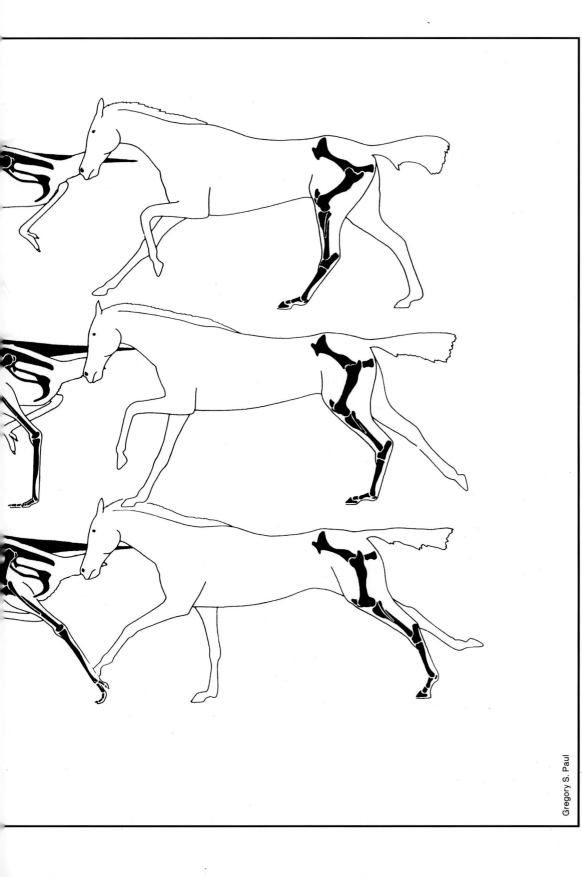

Gregory S. Paul

Dinosaur bone structure seems to indicate that at least some of the great reptiles had warm blood. As this diagram shows, the action of the dinosaur's limbs while running closely resembles that of a horse or an ostrich—both of which are warm-blooded.

Gregory S. Paul

advantage are birds and mammals, both which are warm-blooded. Comparison suggests that many dinosaurs were similarly able to stand erect largely because they were warm-blooded.

Even more telling physical evidence has come from the remains of many predatory dinosaurs discovered over the past few decades. These discoveries call into question the image of dinosaurs as slow-moving plodders, and none more dramatically than the discovery of the dinosaur scientists named

Deinonychus, the notorious "Terrible Claw." This bipedal dinosaur (see pages 60-61) had slender, muscular legs that were perfectly adapted for running. Without a doubt, these fierce predators chased their prey, tearing them with the curving knifelike claws that tipped each foot. Although cheetahs and other warm-blooded mammals hunt in this fashion, cold-blooded animals are not capable of a fierce attack requiring such agility. Their hearts and circulatory systems simply cannot maintain the energy level necessary to sustain such active movement.

"It seems undeniable that Deinonychus and related predators were warm blooded," Bakker states. "But if you look at the structure of the bones of other dinosaurs, you'll see that most or all could also have practiced heat regulation." As scientists using powerful microscopes and other scanning devices have found, modern reptiles have dense, slow-growing bones that are nearly featureless except for rings that resemble the age rings of tree trunks. By comparison, mammals have

Doug Henderson © 1986

What is the truth about the *Allosaurus* (right)? Was it an ancient vulture, too unwieldy to kill its own food? Or was it a fierce and fast-moving predator, tirelessly chasing down its prey? We may never know for sure.

Many of today's scientists reject the old image of dinosaurs as slow-moving, sluggish creatures. As this painting shows, predators such as the *Dilophosaurus* (left) may have been lithe and agile hunters.

fast-growing bones riddled with channels that look like dark holes when magnified. These channels, surrounded by bony tissue and containing blood vessels, are called Haversian systems and were once thought to occur only in warm-blooded creatures. But scientists studying fossilized dinosaur bones have found that they look far more like mammal bones than like those of reptiles. They contain many channels, indicating the presence of an active blood flow similar to that of mammals and birds and providing strong evidence that dinosaurs had warm blood.

To refute this evidence, however, many scientists point out that some reptiles (sea turtles, for instance) do have bones coursed with channels, while the bones of birds and small mammals are comparatively featureless. One feature common to

all animals with channeled bones is that they are relatively large, which may indicate that the structure of bones has more to do with an animal's size than with body temperature regulation.

So the argument continues, with many paleontologists believing that at least some dinosaurs were warm-blooded. Most experts at least now grant that Deinonychus, Oviraptor, and other predators must have had some sort of body-heat regulator that allowed them to hunt with such persistence and agility. Were this so, these dinosaurs may have been very similar in biology and behavior to today's predatory mammals.

The larger dinosaurs, however, may still have been cold-blooded, as are the crocodiles and alligators of today. The enormous sauropods like the Brontosaurus would probably

Allosaurs may well have been warm-blooded. But, like large alligators of today, giant *Sauropods* like this *seismosaur* may have depended on their bulk to insulate them from temperature extremes.

simply not have been able to eat the vast quantities of food that would have been necessary, given their size, to sustain the necessary internal heat regulation.

Study of modern reptiles, in fact, provides evidence that the larger dinosaurs probably maintained warm body temperatures by conserving as opposed to producing body heat. Researchers have found that larger reptiles are able to maintain body temperatures more easily than smaller ones because of greater insulation. The body temperature of a small alligator, for example, follows the temperature of the outside air almost exactly, while that of a large alligator takes much longer to change. Large dinosaurs, their 80-ton (82-metric ton) bodies coated with a mass of insu-

Doug Henderson © 1986

lating fat, would probably have been similarly protected from temporary changes in temperature. As these great reptiles lived in generally warm climates, they may not have been affected by minor temperature alterations, and would not have needed to internally regulate their body temperatures.

The passion of Bakker and others makes the issue of dinosaurs' blood one that may be debated forever. (In 1978, the annual meeting of the American Association for the Advancement of Science hosted so many arguments about heat regulation that a book was eventually published on the proceedings.) "It's nearly impossible to reach a consensus among paleontologists on any issue," Bakker laments. "Certainly not on this one."

Do dinosaurs have any living relatives? Here, an artist depicts the possible evolution of winged dinosaurs into modern-day birds.

DINOSAURS WITH WINGS?

Are there living dinosaurs? Is it possible that a Brontosaurus or Tyrannosaurus still stalks the jungles of Africa or the wastes of the Gobi Desert? The answer is almost certainly no. But, unlike these mythical survivors, possible dinosaur descendants may be easily spied day to day in a big city. Just look out a window at the chickadees clustered around any bird feeder or at the pigeons gathered in the park. You may be looking at feathered, seed-eating, warm-blooded dinosaurs.

No matter how closely we scrutinize a pigeon or a sparrow, we are hard pressed to find any resemblance between these tiny feathered, air-borne birds and massive, scaly, land-dwelling dinosaurs. It would seem to make as much sense if you were comparing a butterfly to an elephant.

Yet all scientists agree that birds are in some way kin to reptiles, if not specifically to dinosaurs. Look at an x-ray of the bone structure of a bird's wing, and you'll see a structure closely resembling a lizard's front leg. (The hoatzin, an odd South American bird, is actually born with reptilelike claws protruding from its wings.) This and other similarities (for example, both birds and reptiles lay eggs) make it clear that today's birds—from hummingbirds to eagles—can claim reptilian ancestors.

Scientists would probably never have considered the possibility that birds descended from dinosaurs if not for a remarkable discovery in

1861, when fossil hunters came upon the bones of a perfectly preserved Late Jurassic creature in a German quarry. Upon its death, 150 million years ago, the strange reptile had fallen into mud that hardened before the skeleton could be destroyed by scavengers or natural decomposition. At first glance, researchers believed that they had the fossil of a small, meat-eating dinosaur similiar to the coelurosaurs, agile bipedal predators that first appeared in the Late Triassic Period. Upon closer examination, however, these scientists made a startling discovery: The reptile was covered with feathers.

This little feathered dinosaur measured about 3 feet (0.9 meters) in length and had thin, fine-boned legs, long, delicate toes, and slim jaws edged with short teeth. Its feathers, their imprints delicately captured in the fossilized mud surrounding the skeleton, bordered both its slender arms and the long bones of its tail. Its discoverers named it *Archaeopteryx* ("Ancient Feather"), and soon found that it shared other characteristics with birds. Most striking was the appearance of a recognizable wishbone, similar to that formed from the uniquely joined collar bones today found in all birds, but in no other animals.

While it was clear that the Archaeopteryx was closely allied with the reptiles, with its sharp teeth, bony tail, and many other similar physical traits, most scientists at first rejected the idea of a specific relationship between this prehistoric bird and the actual dinosaurs. They claimed that both reptiles

If you look at the bones of this little creature, you'll see only a small dinosaur. Take another look, though, and you'll notice the feathers around the arms and tail. It's *Archaeopteryx*—whose discovery in 1861 provided the first clue that birds and dinosaurs were related.

and this birdlike creature evolved from a common ancestor, probably an ancient thecodontian. A direct bird-dinosaur link, however, was at best a weak one.

The doubters' conclusions revolved around one small portion of the Archaeopteryx's anatomy: its wishbone. Although this strange creature's wishbone was of an unusual configuration (resembling a boomerang), it had clearly evolved from a collar bone. The coelurosaurs (the dinosaurs most closely resembling the Archaeopteryx) could not have developed into birds for a very simple reason—they had no collarbones at all.

Debate of this issue continued for many years, until paleontologists in the 1970s made further startling fossil discoveries. They found that Velociraptor and some other coelurosaurs did have collarbones that could well have developed into the Archaeopteryx's wishbone. In fact, most coelurosaurs, some scientists now believe, might have possessed collarbones, which could easily have been overlooked amid many similar bones in a broken-up skeleton.

With the mystery partially resolved, experts began to reemphasize other similarities that existed between the agile coelurosaurs and the ancient bird. Like many modern birds, the coelurosaurs had remarkably light, hollow bones, long necks, very long hind legs, and a backward-facing hind toe (which perching birds use to cling to tree branches). Finally, scientists resolved that the birdlike Archaeopteryx shared so many characteristics with the coelurosaurs that it

was almost certainly related to them. It was, in fact, a dinosaur with wings and feathers.

The debate over the Archaeopteryx's ancestry has been displaced in recent years by equally lively arguments concerning the ancient bird's lifestyle. For instance, scientists differ about the function of their primitive wings, and why, or for what purpose, feathers first evolved from coelurosaur scales. Some argue that feathers helped the dinosaurs conserve heat, while others assert that they provided balance when the animals hunted. Feathers might also have proved an evolutionary advantage by helping the dinosaurs jump further or change direction more rapidly.

Among those who believe the Archaeopteryx' wings were used for flight, debate revolves around how skillful a flier the dinosaur might have been. There's no doubt that Archaeopteryx didn't approach modern birds in the ease and strength of its flight, for it lacked the strong breastbone that serves to anchor the powerful muscles that birds use to flap their wings. The ancient bird may have merely fluttered weakly for short flights from the ground, or soared briefly, buoyed by the wind.

Another argument concerns where the birdlike dinosaurs chose to live. One recent theory proposes that the Archaeopteryx may actually have lived in trees. Not only were its arms edged with feathers, they were also tipped with grasping, sharp-clawed fingers. Some scientists think the creature may have adapted to an arboreal life, climbing into trees with the aid of

In this fanciful rendition, both the *Archaeopteryx's* birdlike and dinosaurlike features are easy to spot. Its thick feathers, grasping feet, and posture all resemble a bird's, but its toothy jaw leaves no doubt of its reptilian ancestry.

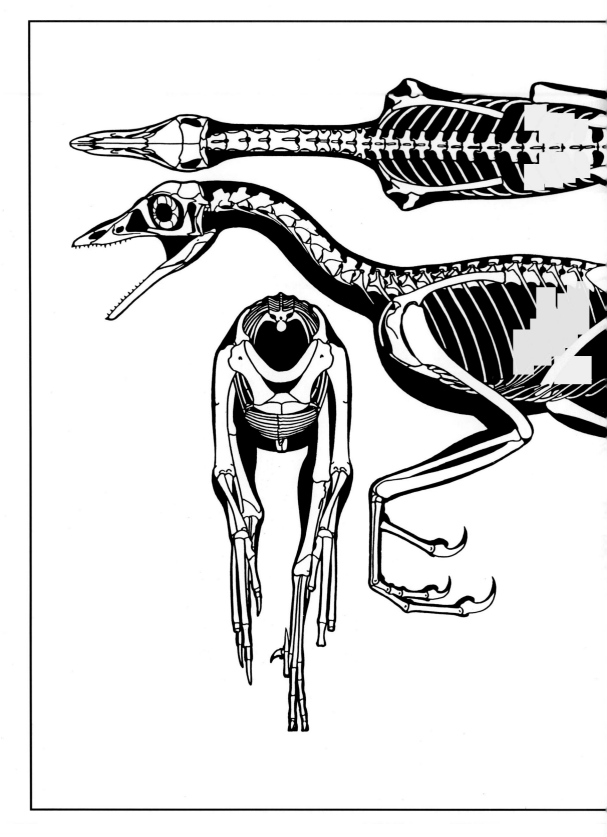

These sketches of *Archaeopteryx*'s skeleton clearly show its similarity to dinosaurs, particularly to the *Coelurosaurs*. But the ancient bird's uniquely modified collarbones, joined to form a wishbone that strengthened its wings, probably allowed it to flutter at least short distances.

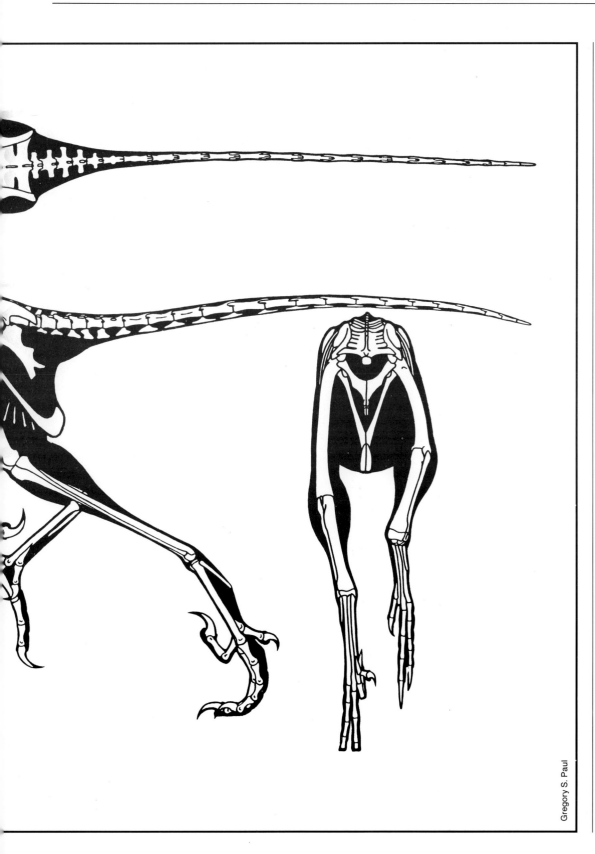

Gregory S. Paul

its strong hind legs and flexible fingers. Or the Archaeopteryx may have used its primitive wings to help lift itself to the lower branches of trees, and then to flutter gently back down to the ground. A shady, leaf-camouflaged environment would have enabled the creatures to elude larger, more powerful predators, while also encouraging the evolution of more extensive feathers for insulation against the cooler temperatures found in a shady arboreal habitat.

Until recently, all the research on early birds was based entirely on the Archaeopteryx, since no other relevant fossils had been found. Then, in 1985, a team of Russian scientists unearthed the skeleton of the *Avimimus,* the Late Cretaceous "Bird Mimic" whose skinny legs and large eyes closely resembled a bird's. Through close study of the Avimimus' skeleton, the scientists have pinpointed some structural features that indicate that this unusual creature may have also sported feathers.

This amazing discovery was soon eclipsed by yet another. In mid-1986, Sankar Chatterjee, a paleontologist at Texas Tech University, reported finding the skeleton of a creature far older and more bird-like than the Avimimus—or even than the Archaeopteryx. "We have named it *Protoavis,* or the 'First Bird,'" Chatterjee says. "It dates from the Triassic Period, more than 225 million years ago, and we believe that it is the true missing link between birds and dinosaurs."

The Protoavis may be the key to a paradox that has long puzzled paleontologists searching to isolate the historical moment when birds evolved from the dinosaurs. "We have always wondered how the Archaeopteryx, living 150 million years ago, could be the first bird, when modern-looking herons, ducks, and other birds showed up only a few million years later," says Chatterjee. "There was simply not enough time for the Archaeopteryx to evolve into those true birds."

The Protoavis, which lived 75 million years earlier than the Archaeopteryx, poses a different scenario. Chatterjee claims that the Protoavis is an indisputable ancestor of today's birds and believes that the Archaeopteryx, on the other hand, is probably only a dead-end branch on the evolutionary tree. Chatterjee explains: "Protoavis had a bird's hollow bones, a well-developed wishbone, a large brain, and distinctively wide eye sockets, as are found in all birds." Even more importantly, it had the muscle-anchoring breastbone that all birds depend on for flight, a feature the Archaeopteryx lacked. And, although no feather impressions were preserved with the Protoavis fossil, Chatterjee believes that small bumps along the fossil forelimbs may provide indication as to where the bird's feathers were attached.

Not all paleontologists are convinced that the Protoavis is really anything more than a previously unknown early dinosaur, and that the Archaeopteryx should indeed be consigned to an evolutionary dead end. But, as Hotton says, "There is no doubt that Protoavis is a bird, and a remarkably advanced and early one."

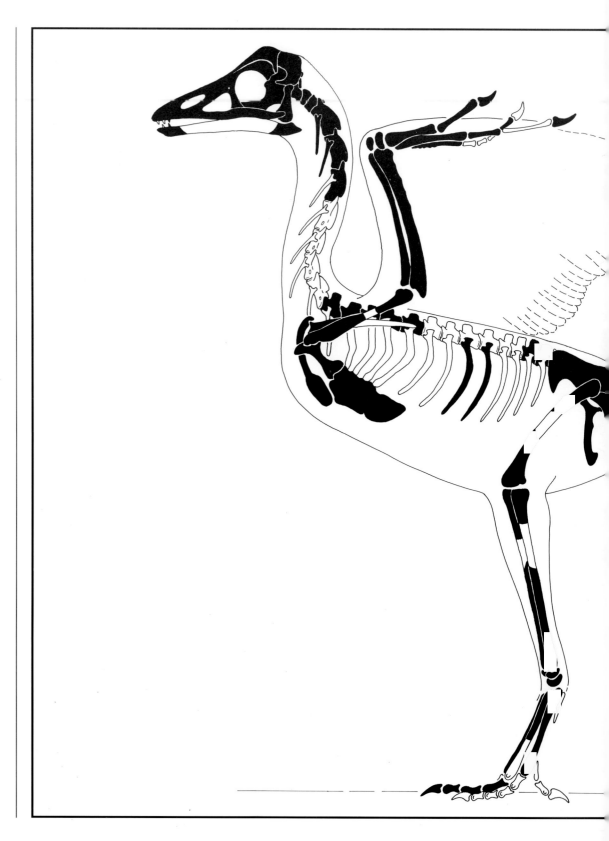

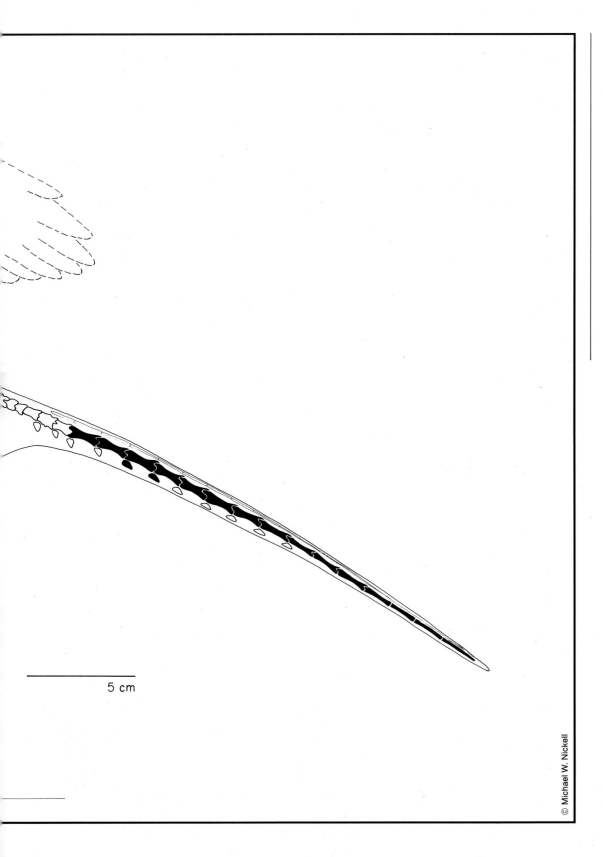

5 cm

Could it be possible then that today's birds are in fact the direct descendants of dinosaurs? Are today's birds, in a sense, living and breathing dinosaurs? If so, they are the last surviving relatives of the great reptiles that ruled in such abundance during the Cretaceous Period. Sixty-five million years ago something killed off all the rest of the dinosaurs—every last duckbill, Triceratops, and Tyrannosaurus. But somehow the birds survived, while their dinosaur relatives died out. How this happened is just one of the questions that makes the great dinosaur extinction the most puzzling—and most fascinating— mystery in paleontology today.

Hollow bones, a well-developed wishbone, and a strong breastbone all show that the recently discovered *Protoavis* was an ancient bird, though its tail and teeth closely resemble those of a dinosaur. These two facts may provide proof that birds evolved from dinosaurs over 200 million years ago.

END OF AN EMPIRE

A solitary reptile stands in a landscape laid barren by a mud flow, a possible partial cause of the dismal end to the dinosaur's 160 million year reign.

Doug Henderson © 1984 Collection of Museum of the Rockies

Lacking a time machine piloted by brave paleontologists, we will probably never know for sure just what caused the great extinction of the dinosaurs. This shouldn't be so surprising. After all, as J. Keith Rigby, Jr., a geologist and paleontologist at Notre Dame University in Indiana, says, "Extinctions happen all the time; if you live, you're going to die."

Still, the death of the dinosaurs, the complete destruction of creatures that seemed so powerful, remains a fascinating puzzle to Rigby and other paleontologists. From studying the layers of rock that make up the earth's geological records, they know that throughout the Cretaceous Period, many dinosaur species were abundant. Duckbills and horned dinosaurs were particularly widespread, as were such non dinosaur reptiles as the flying pterosaurs and the huge swimming plesiosaurs.

"And then, at the border between the Cretaceous and Tertiary Periods 65 million years ago (known as the K-T Boundary), something happened," says the Smithsonian's Hotton. "On one side of the line, you find the fossils of many dinosaurs; on the other side, few or none." And it wasn't just the dinosaurs that died out in that relatively brief period. All pterosaurs and plesiosaurs and hundreds of other animals and plants also became extinct, leaving no descendants. Yet other creatures, including crocodiles, birds, and early mammals, survived. How did this happen?

Scientists in any field love a mystery, and when the dinosaurs' extinction was revealed in the fossil record, paleontologists immediately seized upon the phenomenon and began to propose theories to explain the remarkable event. Today, many of these theories seem simplistic, illogical, or even silly, but over the years most have been seriously considered.

One early theory suggested that as the dinosaurs evolved into larger and larger creatures they simply became too stupid to survive. For example, both the Tyrannosaurus and the Triceratops were among the most gigantic of their kind; perhaps their brains, small to begin with, just didn't grow large enough—leaving the dinosaurs ill equipped to efficiently adapt to a changing world.

The trend toward greater size as the Cretaceous progressed gave rise to another widely held theory, which argued that the great creatures eventually became too heavy to survive. Their bulk, some believed, led to slipped disks and other physical problems that prevented them from finding food or breeding efficiently enough to perpetuate their species.

Another popular explanation is best labeled the "mammal-chauvinist" theory. Small shrewlike and catlike mammals were abundant in the Late Cretaceous, and some scientists suggested that these skulking predators scavenged and ate so many dinosaur eggs that few dinosaur babies were born, dooming the great reptiles to extinction.

All three of these theories (all of which are still taught in schools)

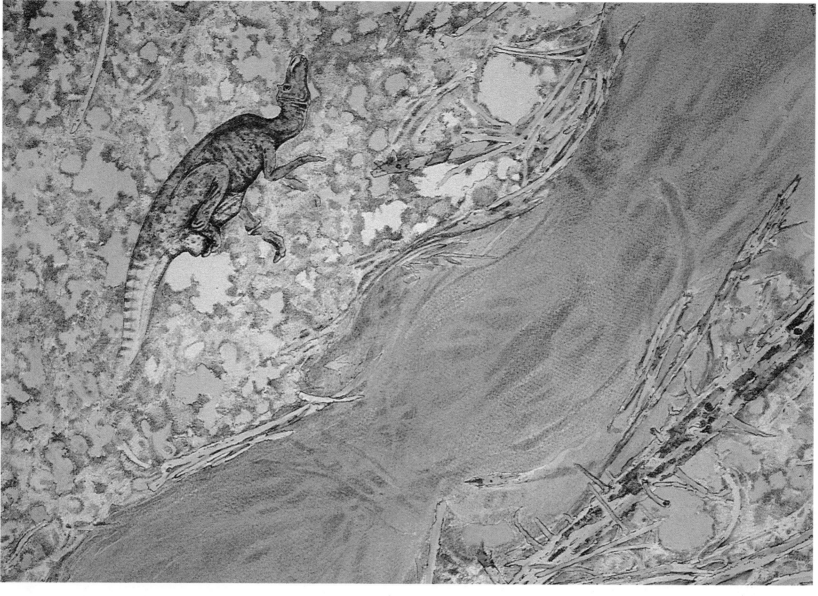

Doug Henderson © 1984

Lizards—like these raiding a *Maiasaura* nest (left)—undoubtedly ate their share of dinosaur eggs. But scientists don't think that egg-eating, by lizards or mammals, had a major impact on dinosaur populations.

No one can prove exactly what caused the great extinction of the dinosaurs. Changes in the climate, erupting volcanoes, and a huge asteroid impact may all have contributed to the end of the ruling reptiles' reign.

suffer from serious flaws. First, there is no evidence that the dinosaurs were ever "too stupid" to survive. In fact, the more we find out about them, the more we discover how varied and adaptable they actually were—after all, they were the dominant creatures on earth for 160 million years. Similarly, the "slipped-disk" hypothesis has no factual foundation; many huge dinosaur species lived quite successfully for millions of years. And the "mammal chauvinist" theory also seems very unlikely. There were simply too many dinosaurs, including some that guarded their eggs from all predators, for egg-eating mammals to make such an impact. Finally, none of these theories explain why so many other animals and plants became extinct at the same time as the dinosaurs.

Having failed to blame the dinosaurs' extinction on the great reptiles themselves, paleontologists then turned to another possibility: deadly changes in the environment of the Late Cretaceous. Scientists know that this was a time of great

Great storms, like this one routing a group of Jurassic *Sauropods*, may have changed the environment of the Late Cretaceous, causing mudslides and flooding and driving dinosaurs away from their age-old food supplies.

changes in the dinosaurs' world. For one, the process of continental drift had wrenched both Gondwanaland and Laurasia into roughly the continents we see today. These geologic shifts may have caused critical changes in the earth's atmosphere and weather. Winters in some areas undoubtedly became more severe, while altered rainfall patterns may have transformed previously swampy areas into deserts and dry highlands into rain-soaked mudholes. The dinosaurs may simply have been unable to adapt to these harsh changes in their environment.

Another environmental extinction theory is based on the evolution of angiosperms, flowering plants and trees that differed from previous primitive vegetation by exhibiting several means of self-preservation. These plants produced poisonous or intoxicating alkaloids with bitter tastes, which deterred many animals from eating their leaves. Unfortunately, the theory goes, dinosaurs, who had evolved at a time of defenseless plants, never developed the ability to perceive the alkaloids' bitterness. Therefore, a steady diet of drug-laden leaves led to the mass poisoning of the duckbills and other plant-eaters. As these dinosaurs died, so did the carnivorous dinosaurs who depended on the plant-eaters for food.

Although the alkaloid hypothesis is still considered at least part of a possible explanation, there are several problems with this theory as it stands on its own. For one thing, the dinosaurs' lack of sensitive taste buds could probably never be proved, but even if there was evidence to support the theory, it still could not explain the fact that angiosperms developed well before the death of the dinosaurs. "For 60 million years dinosaurs seemed to have coexisted quite suc-

cessfully with flowering plants, so it is difficult to blame the reptiles' extinction on alkaloid poisoning alone," says Hotton. Finally, like so many theories, it does not explain what happened to the many other creatures that did not survive past the Cretaceous.

Another recent theory, however, which does take into account the mass extinction of dinosaurs, plesiosaurs and the rest, was inspired by one of the most important, famous, and controversial findings in recent dinosaur-hunting history. In the late 1970s, a University of California at Berkeley geologist named Walter Alvarez was pursuing his studies of continental drift by digging through ancient rock in Italy. Alvarez, just like many researchers in the field, was particularly intrigued by the K-T boundary, which

The *Maiasaurs'* complex social life may have provided protection from predators, but not from the vast environmental changes that occurred at the end of the Late Cretaceous.

showed up at his digging site in the form of a slender layer of red clay between the fossil-rich Late Cretaceous rock and the Paleocene rock laying on top of it.

Interested in this oddly unidentifable layer, Alvarez and his father Luis (a winner of the Nobel Prize in physics) had it analyzed. They found that the mysterious clay contained thirty times the amount of the rare element iridium than normally occurred in rock from the earth's surface. This discovery was remarkable because large quantities of iridium were believed at the time to exist only deep in the earth's core, and the Alvarezes thought it unlikely that so much of the element could have reached the surface from erupting volcanoes.

One possibility, however, did strike the Alvarezes as both a feasible and hugely significant explanation. They asserted that the iridium could have been brought to the earth's surface as the result of a collision between the earth and a huge asteroid rich in iridium, as are all asteroids. According to Luis and Walter Alvarez, the iridium-rich hunk of rock that might have landed on earth at the end of the Cretaceous with the force of thousands of atom bombs would have

sent an enormous dust cloud skyward. This cloud, settling in the atmosphere, would have blocked nearly all sunlight, creating a far cooler and dimmer climate on earth than ever before. This unnatural winter may have lasted for months, or even years. In a dramatic chain reaction, the scenario goes, the first to die were plants, starved of the sunlight essential to photosynthesis. In the ocean, algae and other small vegetation also perished. Plant-eating dinosaurs were suddenly without food, as were small ocean creatures that depended on plant matter. They died, which left meat-eaters—including the pterosaurs and sea reptiles, as well as the remaining dinosaurs—without their prey, so that they, too, passed into oblivion.

According to the theory, the cloud of dust eventually filtered back through the atmosphere and settled on the surface of the earth, leaving the rich layer of iridium found at the K-T boundary. The weather gradually returned to normal, and the plants and animals that had somehow managed to survive the long winter (including crocodiles and early mammals) became the new rulers of a world without dinosaurs.

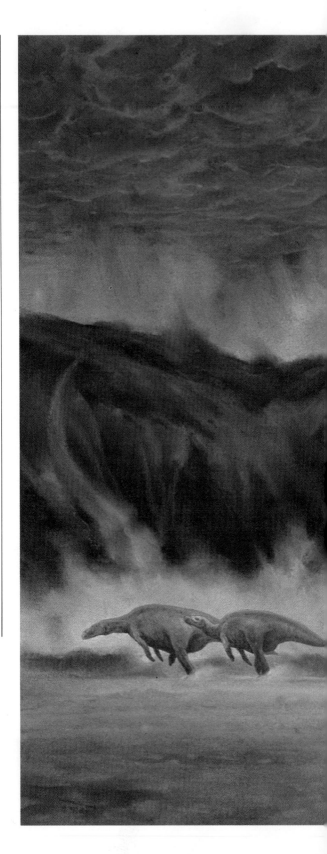

A huge ash-cloud like this one may have doomed entire colonies of *Maiasaurs*, but they also gave scientists the fossils that revealed the "Good Mother Lizards" remarkable social life.

NASA

If, as many scientists believe, the dinosaurs were killed off by some mysterious explosion, one culprit might have been an asteroid—a huge chunk of rock like these, shown circling Jupiter.

Not surprisingly, Alvarez's weather ideas caused quite a stir in the paleontological community. "The Alvarezes woke everyone up," recalls Notre Dame's Rigby. "Their discovery got us all thinking and hunting for clues." And, remarkably, further discoveries served only to support the hypothesis that some cataclysmic event had occurred at this pivotal point in history. Other scientists sampling the K-T boundary sites in North America, New Zealand, Europe, and elsewhere found unprecedented concentrations of iridium along with concentrations of gold and platinum, also found in asteroids, indicating that the dust cloud may have spread around the world. Traces of shocked quartz, a rock containing crystals formed only under the extreme pressure of a violent explosion, were found in the northern United States and in Europe. Obviously, this evidence strengthened the idea that the end of the Cretaceous Period came after an enormous explosion.

In 1983, a new, far more ambitious set of hypotheses appeared, adding to and expanding upon the Alvarezes' impact theory. J. John Sepkoski Jr. and David Raup, a pair of University of Chicago paleontologists, agreed that the extinction of the dinosaurs did occur after some huge object hit the earth. But, they added, their research on ancient marine animals showed that the Late Cretaceous cataclysm was not the only one to occur in geologic history. In fact, a dozen mass extinctions may have happened over the past 250 million years. Most amazingly of all, the scien-

tists claimed that these great extinctions have followed a cyclical pattern. Every 26 million years or so, something has killed off the earth's most abundant creatures. For example, this hypothesis continues, two other events flanked the extinction of the dinosaurs: 91 million years ago, vast numbers of sea urchin species suddenly disappeared, and 38 million years ago, one-celled protozoa were the victims.

The concept of periodic mass extinctions threw the scientific community into a renewed frenzy. Paleontologists, astronomers, and physicists around the world began searching for new clues. Many researchers agreed with the Alvarezes and thought it highly unlikely that any earth-based phenomenon such as volcanoes, or changes in weather, could have caused such widespread destruction; but they found it equally unlikely that large asteroids—most of which circle the sun in a wide band between the planets Mars and Jupiter—could regularly plunge to the surface of the earth. Therefore, researchers turned their attention to another type of extraterrestrial renegade: the comet.

Comets, unlike asteroids, are composed largely of ice; they're a kind of "dirty snowball" traveling through space. They do, however, carry various metals and other elements, including iridium. In their study of comets, scientists have identified an astral phenomenon called the Oort Cloud, a vast sea of comets that surrounds the Solar System. Occasionally, a group of comets is shaken loose from the cloud (perhaps by the gravity of a star passing nearby), and is drawn toward the sun. Some of these comets make just one pass, slingshotting around the sun and then hurtling out of the Solar System. Others, however, fall into a steady orbit, and return again and again (just like the famous Halley's comet). Conceivably, a comet orbiting the sun might also intersect the earth's orbit, resulting in a destructive collision.

Yet scientists were not clear as to why a swarm of comets would leave the Oort Cloud in a regular fashion, every 26 million years or so. The answer, many astronomers thought, had to lie with some as-yet-unknown object passing near to or through the cloud. Richard Muller, a professor of astronomy and physics at the University of California at Berkeley, first came up with a hypothesis to answer this enigma. He suggested that the sun, like half the stars in the galaxy, has a companion star that orbits about it, and that this companion's unique orbit passes through the Oort Cloud every 26 million years, shaking loose a storm that sends one or more comets smashing into the earth.

Muller and his coresearchers named this unseen star Nemesis, after the Greek goddess who punishes the sin of pride. Others dubbed it the "death star." For this "death star" to wreak the havoc attributed to it, it would have to travel an odd, irregular orbit, one that would only take it past the Oort Cloud on rare occasions. Today, Muller and many other astronomers are using high-powered tele-

scopes to search the sky for Nemesis. They believe that it may be a "brown dwarf," a relatively tiny, very cool star that gives off little energy. If that is the case, then it is no surprise that it has escaped notice amid the millions of stars in our galaxy.

Other scientists, rejecting the companion-star theory, are searching the heavens for yet another possible explanation: a mysterious planet at the far end of our Solar System. The presence of Planet X, as it's been named, has long been suspected by astronomers trying to explain the cause of strange orbital variations of the distant planets Uranus and Neptune, variations that, they believe, can only be caused by an unseen planet with a remarkable orbit of its own. Planet X's orbit, their theory states, is usually uneventful, yet every 26 million years, its erratic circuit around the sun takes it near the edge of the Oort Cloud, shaking comets loose and sending them to swoop toward earth.

While physicists and astronomers continue to debate the possible existence of Nemesis or Planet X, paleontologists such as Hotton don't believe that the fossil record supports the idea of cyclical mass extinctions at all. "Throughout history, there have been many great extinctions, but to blame them on some regular, predictable event is pure fancy," he says. "For example, my field of study—the time of the mammal-like reptiles—includes one of the so-called periodic extinctions. But it is clear that these reptiles died out gradually—not because of some orbiting death star."

Some scientists hypothesize that 65 million years ago the earth's collision with a comet, like Halley's Comet, may have helped doom the dinosaurs to extinction.

NASA

Still, though he dismisses the idea of periodic cataclysmic extinctions, Hotton believes that the death of the dinosaurs was probably triggered by a collision between the earth and a rogue comet or asteroid. "Although some people think the dinosaurs were already dying out in the Late Cretaceous, I'm convinced that the collision was the major cause of their extinction," he says. "Why? Because of the mammals."

It is well known that mammals, though they coexisted with the dinosaurs for millions of years, weren't dominant species during the reign of the great reptiles. It was only after the dinosaurs died out that the mammals begin to diversify and gain in numbers. "When extinction is gradual, new species fill empty ecological niches almost immediately," Hotton explains. "But ten million years passed after the Cretaceous ended, and all mammals remained comparatively small in size, leaving many niches unfilled. Then, suddenly, the mammals began to diversify and grow larger at an increasing pace, finally replacing the dinosaurs."

Hotton asserts, then, that the time lag between the dinosaurs' disappearance and the rise of the mammals indicates that the dinosaurs' dying couldn't have been typically gradual, because had it been, the mammals would have been evolving simultaneously and would have been ready, at the time of the dinosaurs' death, to take their place.

Notre Dame's Rigby doesn't agree with Hotton's theory; he be-

NASA

What could have sent a rain of comets hurtling towards the earth? Paleontologists are skeptical, but some astronomers blame Planet X, a mysterious object orbiting beyond Pluto.

lieves that the mammals evolved about as quickly as could be expected after the dinosaurs' extinction. Even more radically, though, while Rigby agrees that some sort of explosion probably occurred, he does not believe that the impact necessarily had *any* effect on the life and death of the dinosaurs, and he has data to support his conclusions. Over the past several years, he and his coworkers (many of whom are his students at Notre Dame) have been exploring a fossil-rich ancient streambed in Hell Creek, Montana. Digging in this isolated area, they have gained fascinating insights into the final years of the dinosaurs. "From what we now know, it seems that the dinosaurs really hit their peak about 100 million years ago, or 35 million years before the end of the Cretaceous, far earlier than many people think," says Rigby. "Then, the earth went through a gradual cooling—and the dinosaurs began to decline, both in species and number."

Rigby has charted this decline at Hell Creek using an intriguing method: the number of dinosaur teeth per ton of rock. "Well before the end of the Cretaceous, we get about 200 teeth per ton, but this decreases markedly as we approach the K-T boundary. In rock dating from just before the impact, we find only 30 to 35 teeth per ton," he points out. This evidence suggests that, contrary to Hotton's doubts, the dinosaurs were dying out significantly before any explosion occurred. And in rock from after the end of the Cretaceous Period—a time when all dinosaurs are

thought to have been extinct— Rigby still finds 18 dinosaur teeth per ton of rock. "There is no doubt that the dinosaurs lived far past the impact, into the Paleocene Period," he states. "Even a million years after the end of the Cretaceous Period, dinosaurs still survived."

According to Rigby's findings, an unnatural winter created by an exploding asteroid or comet simply could not have created the short-term havoc that many scientists still believe was the cause of the dinosaurs' death. "At most, the impact may have added a little bit more pressure to a situation that was already incredibly stressed for the dinosaurs—due to cooling temperatures and other environmental changes," Rigby says. "The impact itself may have been merely a coincidence, rather than an important element in the dinosaurs' story."

Every important discovery, it seems, leads to a raging debate. With every apparent answer arrives both doubts and further questions. Some scientists, such as Bakker, don't believe a collision happened at all. "I have no doubt that the iridium layer and the presence of shocked quartz are the results of intense volcanic activity at the K-T boundary," he states, reminding us that iridium is found at the earth's core, and can be released by volcanoes. Shocked-quartz crystals may also be created by terrestrial pressures.

Several other new theories also aim to explain why the great extinction, in light of recent evidence, was far less sudden and sweepingly catastrophic than previously

Throughout their reign, the dinosaurs' world was a warm, welcoming, and nourishing place. By the end of the Late Cretaceous, however, dinosaurs may have had to wander across a barren landscape in search of food.

thought. Perhaps acid rainstorms pelted the earth for an extended period following violent volcanic activity; or showers of small comets may have bombarded the planet for a million years or more. Bakker himself believes that climatic changes may have precipitated widespread dinosaur migrations. These dinosaurs may have been carrying the germs of deadly diseases that they themselves were immune to. In the areas they migrated to, however, the dinosaurs would have had no defenses against these diseases, and would have sickened and died in droves. (A similar phenomenon took place when European settlers brought smallpox to the New World, decimating the defenseless populations of American Indians.)

Further study is sure to uncover fascinating new secrets etched in fossil and stone, which will displace many now-popular theories. Yet whether or not the ultimate answers to the dinosaur riddle are ever discovered, the hypotheses of countless "dinosaur hunters," whether disputed or accepted, have had their value. "Such creative and inventive ideas as the Alvarezes' don't happen very often," Rigby points out. "Whether we agree with their conclusions or not, we owe them a major debt of gratitude —for they've helped make the past few years among the most exciting in the history of paleontology."

Violent volcanic activity may have sent great clouds of ash skyward, choking plantlife and small animals, and condemning the great dinosaurs to extinction.

Roy Chapman Andrews (seated, second from left) poses with the members of his 1922 expedition to the Gobi Desert in Mongolia.

DINOSAUR HUNTERS PAST AND PRESENT

In an age of seemingly constant fossil discoveries, it is difficult to imagine that, less than a century and a half ago, no one had any idea that the dinosaurs had ever walked the earth. Although people have undoubtedly been stumbling across dinosaur bones and footprints throughout history, prior to the nineteenth century no one realized what they had found.

In 1677, for example, a man named Robert Plot found a bone later identified as having belonged to a dinosaur. Plot, however, thought the bone came from a giant man. He might have made a more accurate guess but for the historical dictates of the church, which declared that the earth was only a few thousand years old.

This, of course, ruled out the existence of ancient animals, including gigantic reptiles. Luckily, Plot drew a picture of the bone; many years later, scientists identified it as the lower thighbone of the carnivorous *Megalosaurus*.

The next famous dinosaur discovery, made in 1822, occurred in a less rigid age. As one of the best-loved tales of dinosaur history goes, one bright day a British housewife named Mary Ann Mantell was strolling down a road in Sussex when she spied a huge fossil tooth protruding from some rubble. Bending down for a closer look, she saw more teeth embedded in the stone. She and her husband, Dr. Gideon Mantell, an avid and knowledgeable fossil collector, knew at once that she had found something unusually important. The first official dinosaur discovery had been made.

Dr. Mantell's recently discovered papers refute this story, saying *he* had actually found the first tooth. Regardless, his conclusions were certainly ahead of their time. He was sure that the teeth were the remains of some huge plant-eating reptile that had lived during the Cretaceous Period—a time when no reptiles were believed to exist. Mantell named his ancient animal Iguanodon, after the iguana, a New World lizard with similar (but far smaller) teeth. He even published a description of what a living Iguanodon must have looked like, though his reconstruction of a heavy, lumpish reptile with a cute little horn on its nose was extremely inaccurate (For example, the horn was later found to be one of the Iguanodon's thumbs.)

Dr. Gideon Mantell (right), an avid British fossil hunter, and his wife, Mary Ann, were the first to find a dinosaur fossil and identify it as belonging to a giant extinct reptile. They discovered the teeth of an *Iguanodon* (far right), a Cretaceous plant-eater.

Mary Evans Picture Library

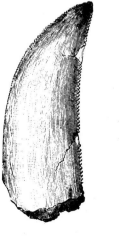

Ann Ronan Picture Library   ref. 5688

Ann Ronan Picture Library   Ref 145/1/309

Another Englishman, geologist William Buckland, was making important discoveries of his own around the same time. In 1824, he described some fossils he had found in a quarry near Oxford six years earlier. Along with finding vertebrae and other bones, he had recovered long, knifelike teeth that were apparently adapted to meat-eating—far different from the grinding teeth of the Iguanodon. Buckland named his discovery Megalosaurus, or "Giant Reptile."

Both Mantell and Buckland's discoveries caused great excitement throughout the British scientific community, spurring a large-scale treasure hunt across the country. This search for fossils soon led to another Mantell discovery; in 1833, he announced the existence of a third giant reptile, which he named *Hylaeosaurus*.

Still, it wasn't until 1841 that anyone hypothesized that these

William Buckland (left), a British geologist, was another major contributor to the fossil-hunting craze that swept across England in the 1820s–1830s. Buckland's first reported find was of the sharp, curving teeth of a *Megalosaurus* (far left), an early *Carnosaur*. The top illustration shows an *Iguanodon* and a *Megalosaurus* in a fight to the death, as seen by a 19th Century artist.

fragments of bone were pieces of a larger picture in world history. At a meeting of the British Association for the Advancement of Science, paleontologist Richard Owen suggested the existence of an extinct group of huge reptiles, creatures whose size and numbers far surpassed anything ever before imagined. He named this group *Dinosauria*, or "Terrible Lizards." Not surprisingly, Owen's first vision of the giant reptiles as hulking beasts that plodded along on four legs was far from the mark. (His reconstructions of the first dinosaurs can still be seen in the Crystal Palace Park in London, which contains huge concrete statues of the Iguanodon and others.) Nonetheless, Owen's courageous theories provided scientists everywhere with the enthusiasm and inspiration to plunge into dinosaur research in earnest.

In the United States, anatomist Joseph Leidy reconstructed by far the most accurate dinosaur skeleton of his time. From bones found in New Jersey he unveiled to the public a plant-eating dinosaur that had clearly stood on its long back legs, a direct contradiction of Owen's and other experts' postulations. Leidy named his dinosaur *Hadrosaurus*; it was a duckbill later found to have been very common in the United States.

The most famous of all early American dinosaur hunters were the scientists Edward Drinker Cope and Othniel Charles Marsh. Their remarkable fossil finds in the late 1800s (amid a heated rivalry still remembered as the "Bone Wars") thrilled and entertained all dinosaur buffs. To put it more

American anatomist, Joseph Leidy (above), showing a closer eye to detail than most other 19th Century scientists, produced the first accurate reconstructions of *Hadrosaurus*, a common duck-billed dinosaur.

While others made the fossil discoveries, British paleontologist, Richard Owen (far left), was the first to postulate the existence of a vast group of giant extinct reptiles, the dinosaurs. Of course, his early reconstructions (left)—which can still be seen in London's Crystal Palace Park—weren't very accurate.

American Museum of Natural History

Edward Drinker Cope (left), along with his bitter rival, Othniel Charles Marsh (right), scoured western North America for dinosaur fossils. Their ''bone wars'' entertained the public for years, but also uncovered fossils of dozens of new species, including *Brontosaurus* and *Allosaurus*.

plainly, Cope and Marsh couldn't stand each other. Their collecting teams worked in secrecy, extracting fossils from rich quarries and ancient streambeds and smuggling specimens back to their labs for examination. At no time did the two hunters exchange information, which sometimes led them to identify dinosaurs of the same species, but to give them different names.

When the two experts began their hunt, fewer than a dozen dinosaur species had been discovered in North America, most in digs along the East Coast. By the time their work was done, however, the two rivals had identified more than a hundred additional species. They achieved such success by being the first to discover the fossil-laden rock of the American West. (Many

Marsh and Cope were the first to find the rich fossil beds of Wyoming and Montana where modern-day paleontologists are still finding fossils today.

of their digging sites in Colorado, Montana, and Wyoming still yield exciting fossils today.) Among their finds were the Brontosaurus and other massive sauropods, the great Jurassic carnosaur Allosaurus, and the Stegosaurus, with its row of armored plates.

Although there haven't been any fossil hunters as colorful as Cope and Marsh since their time, both the American railroad baron, Andrew Carnegie, and the American Museum of Natural History sponsored several major collecting trips early in this century. These expeditions uncovered rich fossil deposits in many western and eastern states, including the massive fossil-riddled rocks that are now preserved as Utah's Dinosaur National Monument.

American Museum of Natural History

American Museum of Natural History

Roy Chapman Andrews (left), was one of the most ambitious fossil-hunters of the early 20th Century. Among his many finds, the most exciting may have been a nest of *Protoceratops* (an early horned dinosaur), complete with unbroken eggs (right).

In 1910, the American Museum and the Canadian government sponsored a group of collectors who unearthed, in the Red Deer River in Alberta, Canada, the remains of countless Late Cretaceous dinosaurs, including the Triceratops and the duckbill Anatosaurus.

Although dinosaur exploration was largely concentrated in North America and Europe until the early 1900s, scientists knew that equally exciting fossil deposits must exist on other continents. After all, the continents had all been connected during the dinosaurs' reign. Yet, in an era that didn't have jet airplanes, the biggest problem was getting to some of the more remote areas of the world most likely to be rich in fossils. Adventurous early explorers journeyed to "darkest" reaches of Africa, Asia, and South America and made discoveries that have added greatly to our knowledge of dinosaur history.

In 1922, for example, a team headed by Roy Chapman Andrews (and sponsored by the intrepid American Museum of Natural History) traveled to the Gobi Desert of Mongolia and made some of the most important dinosaur finds of all time, including the Oviraptor and other remarkable bipedal carnivores, and the Protoceratops, the early horned dinosaur. Even more exciting, along with the bones of the Protoceratops, Andrews found its fossilized eggs, still lying in the nests where they were laid millions of years ago.

More recently, collectors have found many extraordinary dinosaur relics in Africa and Central

Asia—but none odder or more intriguing than the Deinocheirus, the "Terrible Hand" whose enormous arms tipped with wicked claws are all that has yet been discovered. And some of the richest dinosaur beds are in Tanzania. Interestingly, many of them contain dinosaur species similar or identical to those found in North America—providing proof to scientists that the two continents were once joined.

There are still many areas of the world that explorers have not reached because of impenetrable terrain or wicked weather. Much of South America remains inaccessible to this day. The jagged, towering Andes line the continent's western rim, while the dense Amazon jungle blankets vast areas of land. Not surprisingly, fossil finds in these untamed spans of the South American continent have been few and far between. Only in temperate Argentina were earlier collectors able to map out a picture of life during the Age of the Dinosaurs.

Today, however, researchers have been able to penetrate fossil beds in Peru and Brazil, where they have come upon an amazing variety of unusual, and previously unidentified, dinosaurs. In late 1986, a team of Argentine explorers even discovered fossils in the frozen wastes of Antarctica.

Despite the sophistication of modern technology, according to Hotton, dinosaur hunting has not changed much from years past. "The world's come a long way in the last century, but if you want to find dinosaurs, you still have to go into the field and dig for them," he

American Museum of Natural History

U nfortunately, many thrilling fossils lie hidden in harsh, hard-to-reach areas. If Roy Chapman Andrews hadn't ventured into the untracked Gobi Desert, he would never have found the famous *Protoceratops* nest—or a slew of other exciting fossils.

says. "And, remember, dinosaurs usually didn't choose to die in pleasant, easy-to-reach areas." And he paints a rather unromanticized picture of the discovery process. "You have to sift through tons of rock searching for the one piece that may contain an important fossil," Hotton admits. "This fieldwork can be extremely tedious—but it's all worth it."

The chance to uncover evidence that will change our view of the course of dinosaur history is what makes the months spent laboring in frequently severe conditions so worthwhile. For example, J. Keith Rigby, Jr.'s discovery that dinosaurs lived a million years into the Paleocene Period, long after they were thought to have died out, or John Horner's finding irrefutable evidence that some dinosaurs cared for their young.

Sometimes, however, major discoveries are almost missed (and some inevitably have been missed) because of the massive quantities of rock and fossils that collectors must sift through and study. Sankar Chatterjee first thought that the small, light-boned animal that he found amid a rich lode of other fossils in 1984 was merely a baby bipedal dinosaur. "It wasn't until 1986, when we had a chance to study it more closely, that we found that it was Protoavis—the 225-million-year-old ancestor to modern birds," he recalls.

After returning to the laboratory with their collection, today's paleontologists are able to use modern technology to analyze their fossil discoveries much more closely. For example, though our scientists can determine the relative age of a dinosaur by studying the layer of rock in which it was found, more exact dating is achieved by measuring certain long-lasting radioactive elements found within the fossil. Laser scanners attached to powerful computers can determine the amount of wear on a dinosaur's tooth, while scanning electron microscopes can help researchers study the structure of the tiniest fossil by magnifying it tens of thousands of times. Researchers have even used computerized axial tomography (CAT) scans, which are advanced, extremely powerful x-rays widely used in medicine. With this equipment, scientists were able to see through the ancient eggshells of the Maiasaurus, revealing perfectly preserved fossilized embryos.

Yet, no matter how advanced our technology has become, the core of paleontology still involves the search for new fossils. "If you're considering the field, don't think about the odds, because there are none," warns Hotton. "The earth's surface is enormous, and most of it doesn't contain many fossils. But," he adds, "there's always the chance that you'll make the next big discovery—and the thrill when you do is incomparable."

Sankar Chatterjee's discovery of Protoavis—the possible "First Bird"—was one of the most exciting fossil discoveries of all time. Such discoveries are almost always the reward of years of hard work and frustration. The chance of a great find, however, keeps today's paleontologists searching.

C O N C L U S I O N

If you believe that a massive impact killed off the great reptiles in just months—or at most, a few years—then the post-dinosaur world you might imagine would probably closely resemble the popular conception of the devastation wrought by nuclear war. The corpses of dinosaurs and many other creatures, according to this scenario, would have littered the ground and polluted the lakes and oceans. Trees and other plantlife would have been blighted by the unnatural winter brought on by the impact's dust cloud. Cold winds would have continued to whip up clouds of iridium-rich dust, obscuring a sun that shone only dimly.

Whatever caused the great extinction—a "death stars destruction" or slower processes—not everything died out with the dinosaurs. The ichthyosaurs that had ruled the oceans were gone, but many fish survived. So did some lizards, snakes, and amphibians, the ancestors of plentiful descendants today. And though their coelurosaur relatives had disappeared, modern birds also lived through the calamity, in a sky devoid of the pterosaurs that had dominated for so long.

But of the survivors, the true victors in this upheaval of the natural order were the mammals. Most experts admit that the mammals would probably not have developed much beyond the rodentlike and catlike forms found throughout the Mesozoic Era if not for the disappearance of the dinosaurs. Emerging from the 100-million-year struggle to survive against preda-

tors larger, quicker, and more ferocious than they, the smaller mammals found a world filled with opportunity—and took advantage of it. Here were grasslands, swamps, and mountains no longer ruled by the dinosaurs. Here were new food supplies, increasingly abundant as the years passed, with few other animals to compete for them. No wonder the adaptable mammals eventually began to rule the post-dinosaur world.

The mammals' rise to dominance took a long time, of course; nothing in evolution works very quickly. For millions of years, no mammals grew to significant size; the first forerunners of today's whales, bats,

and horses didn't begin to fill ecological niches left open by the disappearance of the dinosaurs and other ancient reptiles until 10 million years after the great extinction. And the earliest ancestors of such familiar creatures as cats and dogs didn't appear until even later, 25 million years after the last dinosaur had died.

What about humans? The very first apelike relatives of today's people seem to have shown up about 5 million years ago, along with the first chimpanzees and gorillas. The earliest *Homo sapiens*—our own species—took far longer to evolve, arriving perhaps half a million years ago. And *Homo sapiens*

sapiens—modern man—date back a paltry 50,000 years. And keep this in mind: The dinosaurs, those "stupid" reptiles that couldn't adjust to a changing world, survived for 160 million years. How much longer is that than the reign of modern man? About 160 million years.

For this humbling perspective on the history of life on earth we owe a debt to the paleontologists who, over the past 150 years, have recaptured the dinosaurs from their ancient, hidden graves. Hotton, Bakker, and many others have brought these remarkable reptiles back to life. As long as their work continues, the dinosaurs will never truly become extinct.

F U R T H E R   R E A D I N G S

Andrews, Roy Chapman, *All About Dinosaurs* (New York: Random House, 1953).

Bakker, Robert T., *The Dinosaur Heresies: New Theories Unlocking the Mystery of the Dinosaurs and Their Extinction* (New York: William Morrow, 1986).

Colbert, Edwin H., *Dinosaurs: Their Discovery and Their World* (New York: E.P. Dutton, 1986).

_____, *A Fossil Hunter's Notebook: My Life with Dinosaurs and Other Friends* (New York: E.P. Dutton, 1980).

Czerkas, Sylvia, ed., *Dinosaurs Past and Present*, Los Angeles County Museum Special Symposium (Los Angeles: LACM Press, 1986).

Fenton, Carroll Lane, *Tales Told by Fossils* (Garden City, New York: Doubleday, 1966).

Howard, Robert West, *The Dawnseekers: The First History of American Paleontology* (New York and London: Harcourt Brace Jovanovich, 1975).

Norman, David, *The Illustrated Encyclopedia of Dinosaurs* (London: Salamander Books, 1985).

Rudwick, Martin J.S., *The Meaning of Fossils: Episodes in the History of Paleontology* (New York: Neale Watson Academic Publications, Inc. 1972). Recently reissued by University of Chicago Press.

Thomas, Roger D.K. and Everett C. Olson, eds., *A Cold Look at the Warm-Blooded Dinosaurs*, AAAS Selected Symposium 28 (Boulder, Colo.: Westview Press, 1980).

Wilford, John Noble, *The Riddle of the Dinosaur* (New York: Alfred A. Knopf, 1985).

Gregory S. Paul

M U S E U M S   A N D   D I S P L A Y S

CANADA

National Museum of Natural Sciences
Ottawa, Ontario

Provincial Museum of Alberta
Edmonton, Alberta

Redpath Museum
McGill University
Quebec, Quebec

Royal Ontario Museum
Toronto, Ontario

Tyrrell Museum of Palaeontology
Drumheller, Alberta

Zoological Gardens
Calgary, Alberta

UNITED KINGDOM

Birmingham Museum
Department of Natural History
Birmingham

British Museum (Natural History)
London

Crystal Palace Park
Sydenham
London

The Dinosaur Museum
Dorchester, Dorset

Hunterian Museum
The University
Glasgow

The Leicestershire Museums
Leicester

Museum of Isle of Wight Geology
Sandown Library
Sandown, Isle of Wight

Royal Scottish Museum
Edinburgh

Sedgwick Museum
Cambridge University
Cambridge

University Museum
Oxford

UNITED STATES

Academy of Natural Sciences
Philadelphia, Pennsylvania

American Museum of Natural History
New York, New York

Buffalo Museum of Science
Buffalo, New York

Carnegie Museum of Natural History
Pittsburgh, Pennsylvania

Denver Museum of Natural History
Denver, Colorado

Cleveland Museum of Natural History
Wade Oval
University Circle
Cleveland, Ohio

Dinosaur National Monument
Jensen, Utah

Earth Sciences Museum
Brigham Young University
Provo, Utah

Field Museum of Natural History
Chicago, Illinois

Fort Worth Museum of Science
Fort Worth, Texas

Houston Museum of Natural Science
Houston, Texas

Los Angeles County Museum of Natural History
Los Angeles, California

Museum of Comparative Zoology
Harvard University
Cambridge, Massachusetts

Museum of Northern Arizona
Flagstaff, Arizona

Museum of Palaeontology
University of California
Berkeley, California

Museum of the Rockies
Montana State University
Bozeman, Montana

National Museum of Natural History
Smithsonian Institution
Washington, D.C.

Peabody Museum of Natural History
Yale University
New Haven, Connecticut

Pratt Museum
Amherst College
Amherst, Massachusetts

University of Michigan Exhibit Museum
Alexander G. Ruthven Museums
Ann Arbor, Michigan

University of Wyoming
Geological Museum
Laramie, Wyoming

Utah Museum of Natural History
University of Utah
Salt Lake City, Utah

I   N   D   E   X